MY LIFE ON YOUR FARM

MY LIFE ON YOUR FARM

Anthony Parkin

Foreword by Ted Moult

FARMING PRESS LTD
Wharfedale Road, Ipswich, Suffolk IP1 4LG

First published 1983

ISBN 0 85236 135 1

Acknowledgements

The author and publishers wish to acknowledge with thanks the help of the following who gave permission to reproduce photographs: Mrs M. Parker, Mr Peter Smith, the *Farmers' Guardian*, Mr Peter Williams, Mrs Pamela McCormick and Mr Eddie Straiton.

Thanks are also due to Messrs Hamish Hamilton Ltd for permission to quote from *Usage and Abusage* by Eric Partridge, and to the *Birmingham Evening Mail* for permission to quote from Peter Laud's article.

Phototypeset by Galleon Photosetting, Ipswich
Printed in Great Britain by The Garden City Press Limited

Foreword by Ted Moult

I can hardly believe that nearly twenty-five years have passed since I first met Anthony Parkin when he came over to the farm to invite me to introduce *A Living From the Land* for a few months. This was my first experience of 'live radio', a weekly event at the old studios at Broad Street on Wednesday lunch-time. Although I cannot remember making any significant contribution during the half-hour or so of the programme, I did, at least, learn how to 'get out on time' before the weather forecast.

Since then Anthony Parkin's presentation and programme matter have left me addicted to *On Your Farm*. I have tried various treatments but my wife thinks that my condition is incurable. Formerly I used to listen with some difficulty in the milking parlour, to the accompaniment of fizzes and metronomic ticks—all making it very hard to concentrate. Since I believe that radio should not merely be heard, but listened to, milking always took longer on Saturdays because *On Your Farm* slowed the job down.

Then there is the benefit of having met Parkin, the man. His somewhat undemonstrative demeanour conceals a person of strong and compassionate nature. His conscientious approach, exemplified in his career at the BBC, is amply illustrated in this book. Never shrinking from raising controversial issues, Tony is always fair-minded and straight, but not without an all-pervasive sense of humour—which I am sure has prevented him from going bonkers under the circumstances. Besides relieving some of the pressures on farmers, he can be credited with providing a degree of enlightenment that some of the more reactionary ones certainly needed.

Tony's great achievement has been his continual up-dating of *On Your Farm* so that it is always as fresh as a forkful of silage on a freezing winter morning and, of course, to attract and maintain a large non-farming audience. If *On Your Farm* is addictive to those in the farming community and this book required reading for them, both the programme and the book present to outsiders absorbing pictures of today's farming. Farming is on the defensive more at present than at any time I can remember. Even those engaged in agriculture do not share the same outlook; indeed the industry is so diverse that it can hardly be lumped together. Corn versus stock, tenant versus landlord, are just two examples of varying interests. As the shrinkage of the number of farm businesses accelerates there will be an inevitable clash of views between established farmers and the growing number of frustrated, landless, would-be farmers. Maybe we shall realise when the structure of the rural economy is altered beyond recognition that we needed our countryside population more than the short-term profitable exploitation of the land. Just as in forestry, the woods may become more important than the trees—who knows?

Certainly farming is changing, and during his own thirty years of agricultural journalism Tony has borne as much witness as anyone to those changes. For instance, in these days of super-comfort cabs, sound-proofed and all, it is hard to imagine how the general consideration for the farm worker has changed. Picture the scene a few decades ago: a man wearing a bran bag fastened around his shoulders with a horse nail is standing on a tractor which is pulling a converted horse-drawn mowing machine, mowing thistles in the pouring rain. He is standing because there is no seat on the tractor. Asked by an onlooker why he did not purchase a seat for his labourer the farmer replied, 'I don't pay my men to sit down.'

A far cry from today's conditions! And no doubt a change of which Tony Parkin – himself formerly a farm labourer – would approve. Many of his views are deftly incorporated in this book and especially strong are his ideas of standards and morality—certainly Auntie never had a more loyal servant.

As for his modest description of being called by variations of his proper name; all I can offer is what happened when he and I called in at a local pub.

'This', I said to a local farmer, 'is Tony Parkin.'

'What!', he replied, '*the* Tony Parkin!'

Ticknall, 1983 E. W. MOULT

Preface

'Writing a book,' my good friend and neighbour Roger Judd warned me, 'is nothing at all like doing a programme.' He produced the apt analogy of giving an organ recital, which he frequently does, and making a record which he had recently accomplished. 'People hear one of your whimsical remarks in *On Your Farm* and think that it is just Tony having one of his flings. Similarly they may listen to one of my pieces, perhaps wonder why I took it so fast—and forget it. Cut a disc or write a book and you're in a completely different ball game.'

To him and to various others who read the manuscript, none of whose guidance I took, thank you. Perhaps the soundest advice came from my secretary, Ann Stephens. 'Since they are all telling you to do different things, why don't you write the book you want to write?' So I did and here it is—warts and all.

It would not have been possible without the help of my wife, Wendy, who cheerfully did all the work around the place while I carried on typing. And I must also pay tribute to my faithful Imperial 'Good Companion' which I bought for a tenner (complete with Egyptian pound sign) from some folk returning from the Middle East nearly thirty years ago and on which I must since have typed several million words.

Books often start with an assurance that none of the characters is real and that the story is totally fictitious. In this book all the characters are genuine and everything described actually took place. Where I have veiled the identity or blurred the location it is simply to avoid embarrassment, often mutual.

To those whom I have missed or mis-represented—sorry. Like my programmes this book attempts to be honest and where it falls short all I can do is to apologise in advance.

Tenbury, 1983 A. PARKIN

List of Plates

ONE

What Time Did You Say?

If anyone had told me when we launched *On Your Farm* as 'a weekly review of the agricultural scene' in 1964 that I should still be producing it twenty years later—I would not have been at all surprised. That is exactly what I hoped would happen. I joined the BBC in 1960 to produce farming programmes and as far as I was concerned that was all I wanted to do.

If there has been any surprise I suppose it is that the programme has emerged virtually unscathed through all the changes and developments which have taken place in broadcasting over the years. Apart from a couple of insignificant shifts of five minutes in the starting time, from a quarter past seven to ten past and then back again, *On Your Farm* has been broadcast every Saturday (apart from a few Christmas Days) from the very first week.

Yet millions have never heard it and many of them never will. It is not one of those programmes which you either love or hate, so much as one which your lifestyle either exposes you to or denies you. One of the most embarrassing experiences, and one which I suffer all too frequently, is to be introduced at a party by a devotee of the programme (and they can be exceedingly devoted) to a stranger who has not only never heard it but never heard of its existence. The conversation, to my increasing mortification, goes something like this:

'Well, no need to tell you who this is,' from our well-meaning friend, followed by an interrogative grunt from the third party.

'Saturday morning?' he persists. The third party is totally bewildered and looking round for some means of escape. I am looking for a hole to drop through.

But our friend ploughs on: 'You know. The farming programme. On the radio. Quarter past seven.'

At this the third party stops searching for another drink long enough to exclaim: '*What* time did you say? Good God, man, I'm fast asleep then. Don't get up till ten on a Saturday.' We then discover a mutual interest in C. P. Snow or Thomas Hardy and *On Your Farm* is discreetly forgotten.

Seven-fifteen on a Saturday morning is not everyone's cup of tea although that is exactly what a lot of our listeners confess to be drinking while they listen to us. The extension of the five-day week, the switch from livestock to arable, the increase in alternative channels which have taken place since the programme started ought to have deprived us of listeners—and yet we often attract an audience approaching a million. And this at a time when a lot of folk are sleeping off Friday night and those who are awake have the choice of three, four, sometimes five other radio stations, not to mention breakfast television.

Who are they then, these insomniacs who start their weekends by listening to this seemingly esoteric programme? What makes them switch on and what do they have in common?

Well, to begin with it is by no means esoteric. Its subject is the most basic, the most fundamental, the most essential of all our activities—the production of food. At a pinch we could manage without cars, without carpets, without Concorde even, but we would not last long without food. The one thing which unites all the people who listen to *On Your Farm*, the old and the young, the rich and the poor, townsfolk and countrymen, is that they all eat. And most of them use the countryside for their recreation. Farming is what lies at the very centre of these activities—it is about producing food and the effect on the environment of producing that food.

As concern has increased for the way our food is produced and processed and also for the changes that are taking place in the countryside, so interest in *On Your Farm* has grown.

In a way the programme has outgrown its title which suggests a practical guide to those who grow barley and milk cows. While we count many tens of thousands of practising farmers among our listeners they no longer sit by the radio with a pencil and paper waiting to take down seeds mixtures or feed rations. The programme these days is *about* farming rather than *for* farmers.

Agricultural broadcasting in this country has a long history going way back into the nineteen-twenties when an announcer (presumably in a dinner jacket) solemnly read the fatstock prices every night. Well, plus ça change, as far as that goes; they are still read, daily but now every morning, in *Farming Today*. It was during the Second World War that farm radio really took off. We were desperately short of food, newsprint was rationed and radio was the ideal way of reaching what always has been and always will be a fragmented and isolated community. After the war farming's key role in the national economy was recognised by the passing of the 1947 Agriculture Act. Farming boomed, so did agricultural radio and later television programmes; by 1960, when I joined the BBC, there was an agricultural producer in each of the Corporation's regions with the headquarters of the unit in Birmingham. I took over the Midland Region programme which, in those days, serviced a wasp-waisted area stretching from Herefordshire in the west to Norfolk in the east. The programme was called *A Living From the Land* and was jokingly, and in those days justly, dubbed 'A Damn' Good Living From the Land'.

On Your Farm was then the title of the weekly programme broadcast for the South-East region from London. In 1964 it was decided to wind up this programme and start a new network programme from Birmingham out of which other regions could opt if they wished. As its producer I felt that a new programme should have a new name and suggested 'First Furrow' which was capable of interpretation in various ways to denote an early-morning programme or one which set out to break new ground. However, the powers that be (and they were very powerful in those days) decided otherwise. I was told that it was because the announcers had announced that they would find it difficult to say 'First Furrow'; I think the real reason was that London, having yielded up its own regional farming programme, felt it was retaining something in keeping the old title *On Your Farm* going.

I should have fought but I had had a very tough year, the sort of year which, in retrospect, makes you wonder how you coped. The previous summer my wife had died suddenly leaving me with three children, the youngest of whom was only two. I carried on producing and presenting my weekly radio programme, appearing regularly on our regional television magazine and, for the first six months of 1964, was also producing the Sunday television programme *Farming* while its regular producer was engaged on a special series. I was also trying to set up the new Saturday morning *On Your Farm* as well as look after my family in the face of resistance from a series of unsuitable housekeepers. So I did not fight as hard as I should have done to change the programme's name which now has a somewhat anachronistic ring to it. However, rather like Roy Plomley's 'Desert Island' which appears from his descriptions to be more like a Garden of Eden, what is in a programme is more important than what you call it.

The contents of *On Your Farm* have changed gradually but fundamentally since that first Saturday morning at the end of August 1964. In those days we were still addressing ourselves mainly to the farming fraternity although conscious of the over-the-shoulder audience we had inherited from previous farming programmes. We were still carrying quite a lot of purely advisory and educational material – talks on how to avoid calf scour and the pros and cons of cow cubicles, that sort of thing – and phenomena like the annual farm price review tended to be examined through the eyes of the farmer rather than those of the general public. But things were changing fast. Farming was moving out of an era of too little food into one of potentially too much and some aspects of the technological revolution behind it were causing concern. Already Rachel Carson's attack on the abuse of agrochemicals, *Silent Spring*, had been published in this country and a few months after the new *On Your Farm* went on the air another book which was destined to shake intensive livestock production from top to bottom came out—*Animal Machines* by Ruth Harrison. This was followed shortly afterwards by Elspeth Huxley's *Brave New Victuals* and, a good deal later, by Marion Shoard's polemic, *The Theft of the Countryside*. The last three were all reviewed in the programme and their implications discussed at length on a continuing basis, much to the chagrin of farmers who felt that in *On Your Farm* they had, or perhaps I should say, thought they ought to have, a mouthpiece for their own viewpoints. At the time when pressure groups were gathering support in the areas of the use of chemicals, animal welfare and conservation we were joining the EEC, so that attention was focused on the price of food and the cost of encouraging farmers to produce and sometimes over-produce it. All of these issues had to be taken on board as the programme developed.

The other factor which led to a steady change in the format was the evolution of the daily early morning *Farming Today*. Having started as little more than a bulletin of market prices it developed into a sophisticated programme which analysed and interpreted these trends, had a considerable technical content and dealt with agricultural news on a day-to-day basis. This relieved *On Your Farm* of its role as a purveyor of farming news and enabled it to move from a magazine programme with six or seven short items to one dealing in depth with a single subject where this was justified. Thus, imperceptibly I would like to feel, *On Your Farm* has reacted to what has been going on around it to the point where it deals less now with the technical and practical and more with the political, sociological and, at times, philosophical aspects of agriculture. At the same time it provides a forum for dialogue between producer and consumer, between town and country.

So while we still report on the National Farmers' Union AGM, for example, I would tend to choose for discussion these days the topics which involve the great British public as taxpayers, consumers, ramblers or simply as students of human behaviour rather than deal with those of interest only to farmers. A motion urging that 'dressed carcase weights of lambs and clean sheep presented at liveweight certification centres under the Sheep Variable Premium Scheme be determined by the application of a fixed killing-out percentage to their actual weights' is unlikely to be featured in *On Your Farm*, being of no interest at all to the non-farming public. One calling on 'Her Majesty's Government to support the call for a real increase in the price of agricultural products at the forthcoming Price Review . . .' however, brings in all those who may have to help pay, through their taxes, for a price increase. So it may well find its way into the programme because it is of interest both to farmers and to the public at large. A resolution calling on the NFU to 'continue vigorously to support all reasonable methods of intensive livestock production . . .' would almost certainly find a place, opening up as it does the whole question of so-called factory farming.

One of the questions frequently asked is how the BBC can justify so many agricultural programmes. Besides *On Your Farm* there are the early-morning *Farming Week* and *Farming Today* and Sunday's television *Farming* (which in 1982 celebrated its twenty-fifth year) plus all the Scottish, Welsh and Ulster output. I think the short answer is that the public likes them. The listening and viewing figures have been consistently high and the audience reaction index has remained good.

I think the public likes them for a variety of reasons. To begin with they are about something which involves everyone: as I said earlier, everyone eats, nearly everyone uses the countryside, and farming stands fair and square in the middle. Then there is the strong vein of nostalgia which does not have to be specially catered for; it is there in the people, the accents, the locations, the jobs. I get hundreds of letters beginning, 'I'm not a farmer but my grandfather was', or 'I always wanted to be', or 'I've always spent my holidays on farms' and so on. Listening to *On Your Farm* enables these people to farm vicariously without having to risk getting a bad back or suffering a poor harvest.

What other single subject could take you into the Welsh hills, the Fens, the Weald of Kent, the Cumbrian Fells, the Somerset moors, the Scottish glens and to the lakes of County Fermanagh? Talking to real people about real things. Not posturing politicians or cardboard figures mouthing second- and third-hand opinions but men and women who are risking their money and dealing at first hand with livestock and the soil, with wind, rain, sun, frost and drought to produce the most basic commodity on earth—food. Add science, politics, machinery, disease, sociology, markets, economics, labour and a few dozen other elements and you begin to discern the shape of the thing we call agriculture.

Sometimes the question is asked more pointedly, as it was by Jack Jones when he was general secretary of the Transport and General Workers Union. Why, he asked, casting an eye at our farming output, could there not be a regular series on the transport industry? More recently Tony Benn, in one of his periodic attacks on the media, referred specifically to *Farming Today* when he complained in *The Guardian*, 'There is no programme called *Trade Unionism Today*. There is not even *The Scargills—an everyday story of union folk*.' I certainly would not argue against more specialist programmes, seeing how successful they seem to have been with agriculture. Let us try them and see if they can beat the thirty-odd years of *The Archers*, the quarter-century of *Farming* and the thousand *On Your Farm*s which, I hope, we shall soon have notched up.

Perhaps the most difficult question to answer is 'who is *On Your Farm* aimed at?' I would find it very difficult to produce an Identikit of our target listener. The title of the programme and general presentation suggest an agricultural audience. Yet we think that half the audience has no direct involvement with farming at all. I suppose that I aim the programme loosely at the agricultural community but take into account in the choice and treatment of subject matter the large element of 'eavesdroppers'. The agricultural community goes way beyond farmers; it includes not only farm workers and landowners but also vets and country bank managers, millers and maltsters, feed reps and machinery dealers, farm college lecturers and Ministry advisors, country parsons, research workers, agricultural economists—you could go on for ever.

We are under constant persuasion from some of the pressure groups I referred to earlier to aim the programme more at the general public. I think that this would be wrong and not in their long-term interests. Although it is true that we assume our audience understands what makes farming tick – we expect them to know in broad terms what the Common Agricultural Policy is about and we do not explain what a heifer is – it is my impression that part of the attraction for the non-farming section of the audience is the feeling of listening in to someone else's programme. The intelligent eavesdropper can glean far more about what is going on in agriculture and what farmers' real attitudes are than they would in a programme specially tailored for them. Anyway the formula seems to work which, in itself, is a good reason for not changing it.

TWO

OBs But Not Obese

The first edition of the new-style *On Your Farm* was an ambitious one. I wanted to start on a high note and decided on a live OB (outside broadcast) from Rowland Tyler's farm at Barrowden in Rutland. It was the middle of harvest and, in addition to discussing how Rowland was getting on with his own wheat and barley, I had arranged for area progress reports from my colleagues Ken Ford in the north, James Thorburn in the south-west and John Greenslade in the south-east. To complete the picture we also had a piece from Norman Hicks, then Business Editor of *Farmers Weekly*, on the cereal market throughout the country. David Richardson, the Norfolk farmer with whom I have worked so closely and happily for twenty years, was with me and introduced that very first programme.

The idea was to put over material of some interest and consequence against the fascinating background of a real farm at quarter past seven on a Saturday morning with a day's combining ahead of them. We parked our OB vehicle in the attractive stable yard near the house and laid out cables with microphones to two locations. We also had a Land Rover fitted with a transmitter, and we could broadcast from this vehicle either while driving or when it was stationary. David opened the programme from one of the microphones which was situated in the yard alongside a combine which two of Rowland's chaps were busy greasing. He chatted to them for a few minutes and then, while he moved to the next location, I brought in the reports from other parts of the country. By this time David was with Rowland in one of the buildings round the yard watching a winnower at work. They then got into the Land Rover, swapping mikes, which enabled them to keep talking, and drove to another set of farm buildings a quarter of a mile away where the drier was housed. After discussing various aspects of corn drying they then set off for a field of barley which was to be harvested that day where they were joined by the County Advisory Officer, David Laurance, a man of great ability and charm who was to die tragically early a few years later. To cover the gap between the drier and the barley field, which was half a mile away, David handed back to me and I brought in Norman Hicks' report on the cereal market.

It all went like a dream and got the new series off to a spectacular start. My lasting memory of the programme was standing in the yard by the OB vehicle, headphones on, listening to David and Rowland Tyler talking about malting barley, and watching my secretary Jane Dick pumping her way past on a borrowed bicycle, stop-watch round her neck, clipboard under her arm, on her way to the next location in the grain store.

The BBC radio production secretary is a remarkable animal. No producer would get far without one—especially on OBs. In addition to all the usual secretarial skills they need to be au fait with green lights, red lights, stop-watches, clipboards and cues, and on nodding terms with tape recorders, microphones and windshields. They have to be good at getting rid of people you do not want to talk to as well as persuading reluctant people into thinking that they do want to talk to you. They get given all the rotten jobs to do like hanging (often physically) on to people in the street who do not particularly want to be interviewed and telephoning people we have interviewed to tell them that their contribution is not going to be broadcast.

Jane was one of a series of splendid girls who have helped me with programmes, some of whom stayed five years and more. I remember Jane particularly because she had a habit of getting into unusual situations such as the time we were planning a live OB from the Shropshire and West Midland Show at Shrewsbury. We went up the previous evening to sort everything out and I stopped outside our hotel briefly so that Jane could warn reception that we might not check in until late. Five minutes passed but there was no sign of her so I went in to see where she was. Still no sign and the girl at reception assured me that she had not been to the desk. Suddenly she appeared looking extremely discomposed and while we drove on towards the showground she told me what had happened. As she walked through the hotel door she had been hailed by a woman with the words: 'Ah, there you are. Thank heaven you've come. Quick, this way.' Thinking that this was the warmest hotel welcome she had yet experienced she allowed herself to be propelled into a roomful of girls in various stages of nakedness. 'Hurry up and get undressed,' she was told. 'We haven't much time.' The explanation proved unexpectedly simple. They were holding an Oxfam fashion show at the hotel that evening. Eight of the nine models had arrived and one was missing. The organiser could be forgiven for assuming that Jane was the ninth. A tall, willowy blonde, she would have graced the front cover of any issue of *Vogue*.

Both before and for about five years after we started the Saturday *On Your Farm*, we used to broadcast a lot of programmes from the agricultural shows at Wednesday lunchtime. (Until the ending of regional radio, *On Your Farm* was repeated in some regions on Wednesdays.) They were enormous fun to do and made very good listening as well as being good public relations for the BBC and the programme itself. The show secretary would usually bend over backwards to give us a good site and while we were not broadcasting – and sometimes while we were – we had a stream of visitors, many of them listeners to the programme. We would have the familiar green BBC OB vehicle as a base guarded by the equally familiar uniformed commissionaire who would set up his white rope cordon round the area and endeavour to keep the children out. 'Anyone important here?' they would ask, brandishing autograph books. 'No,' we would reply, truthfully, and they would go away in disbelief.

We would go the evening before to find interesting features and personalities, returning early the next morning to finalise the arrangements and perhaps record one or two interviews which could not be done live. The difficulty was in squeezing a show which could hold your attention for one or two days into thirty minutes' broadcasting. Everyone wanted longer than we could give them. I remember a Canadian Mountie, who was part of the grand ring attraction at one of the shows; I had mentally allocated him a minute and a half. He talked about the Mounties for ages over a glass of beer and then said: 'How long is your programme?' I said: 'Half an hour.' He scratched his head and looked thoughtful. 'I suppose that might be long enough,' he said at last. A similar misunderstanding took place once when I telephoned a woman in Cumbria whom I wanted to interview briefly for one of the 'Taking the Pulse' editions of *On Your Farm*. I was trying to persuade her to give us her views on common land on which she was an expert. 'How long would the interview be?' she enquired. I did not have the heart to say two minutes (actually you can say quite a lot in two minutes—I think Lincoln defined democracy in his Gettysburg speech in one and a half), so I said: 'Oh, four to five minutes.' There was silence for a second or two and then she replied: 'Forty-five minutes, you say? Yes, I think we might be able to get it into that.'

I used to take one or two trusty broadcasters with me to help with the programme. Phil Drabble often came and was one of the most reliable as well as companionable folk with whom I have ever worked. His friendly, easy-going manner over the air concealed a tough, professional approach to the briefest of interviews or most trivial of assignments. Nothing was left to chance. He often reminds me of how I persuaded him to climb a tall wooden tower at the Three Counties Show at Malvern one year so that he could open the programme with a bird's-eye view of the showground. He did the job impeccably, as always, and failed to let me know until afterwards that he suffered from vertigo in the process.

To emphasise the fact that the programme was live and that the show was actually going on round us I used to get a local journalist to feed us during the transmission with the latest results of the livestock judging which was then in full swing. Although we paid a fee for the service, I am not sure that we were always popular with the local press who rather resented the way in which the BBC was given special treatment by the show organisers. So it may have been slightly more than accidental that one of the slips I was handed to read out during a programme ran something like this:

'And the prize for the best Welsh Black went to Mr Arwyn Ap-Cynan Llewellyn-Llewellyn of Bwlchydderwen Farm,

Eglwyswrw with his cow Llanllwchalarn Cwmdeuddwr 2nd.'

Certain things in life are destined to remain a total mystery to me and one of them is the technical aspect of broadcasting. I do not mean how to work a tape recorder or where to hold a mike but recondite matters such as kiloHertz and that sort of thing. Had I been better informed I should not have felt such an idiot as I did when, just as we were preparing to go on the air at the Staffordshire Show, a man rushed up demanding to know what wavelength we were broadcasting on. Not just any man, it turned out. He was an aide to the noble lord who was the show president that year and whom we had interviewed earlier in the morning. Not unnaturally he wanted to hear the programme which included his contribution. A transistor radio had been found for him but no one knew where to find Midland Region. 'Quick, run over to the BBC caravan; they'll know,' someone had said. The trouble was that we did not know. With vital seconds ticking by we all began looking for a copy of the *Radio Times*. No one could find one. I shall never forget the look of sheer incredulity on the man's face when we told him we just did not know. How on earth, he seemed to be wondering, could we transmit a programme without knowing what wavelength to put it on.

Agricultural shows are jolly affairs and music often forms part of the atmosphere. Without asking permission and without incurring complaints from anyone I had been in the habit of recording snatches of music from the bands playing at the shows and using them in the programme to convey the spirit of the occasion. I remember one day returning to our mobile studio with a recording of a military orchestra and playing it to a colleague, the doyen of Pebble Mill's OB engineers. He listened carefully and admitted it was not too bad but insisted that he could achieve a better result. He set off with a tape-recorder that was bigger than mine, a superior microphone, a microphone stand, headphones and yards of cable and proceeded to set these up near the bandstand. The orchestra played on until the conductor, in one of his periodic flourishes, happened to catch sight of what was going on. He tapped his baton on his music rest and the music stopped. Our engineer took off his headphones, satisfied with the level but wondering why the band had ceased playing. He did not remain in ignorance for long. Had we made arrangements? If not, no recording. There were about thirty players in the band and at Musicians' Union rates it would have swallowed up the *On Your Farm* budget for weeks. The MU can teach most trade unions a thing or two when it comes to protecting its members. So we had to manage without music that day.

There were times when I got hauled in to help another producer, usually when I was hoping for a day off to look round a show. It is amazing how little one actually sees of a show when one is working there. Sometimes I have spent four days at the Royal Show without being able to say I have *seen* it. So a few days before I was hoping for a day without a microphone the telephone would go. 'Are you going to be at the Royal Welsh next week?' It is my colleague in Bangor, responsible for Welsh farming broadcasts. 'I wonder if you could help me with my programme on Tuesday. Nothing much, just a few interviews.'

One year, when I had reluctantly agreed to give a hand, I found myself standing outside the BBC compound at Builth Wells with a microphone in one hand, a stop-watch in the other and a pair of headphones. 'We'll come over to you two or three times during the programme,' the producer had said: 'Just talk to some of the passers-by. About one-thirty or two minutes each time, OK?' What he had not told me was that, although I had plenty of mike cable, I only had about six feet of spare cable to my headphones. Every time I moved forward to find a victim the crowd parted and I was brought up short by a sharp tweak on the ears. I could not take the things off—they were my umbilical cord to the mobile studio. Without them I would have no idea of when I was to go into action. Wondering how I was going to cope I heard the presenter saying: 'Well, Tony Parkin's outside our mobile studio here at the Royal Welsh waiting to talk to some of this year's visitors. Over to you, Tony.' I started ad-libbing about the weather and the flapping of the canvas, the fluttering of the flags, the scene in the grand ring and, above all, the people. 'What a crowd,' I said as I tried to get near enough to one of them to talk. Just one of them would do but, no, they formed a neat semi-circle about three feet away from me, giggling and nudging one another. But they had not reckoned with the power of the BBC. Suddenly, from behind them, came the figure of our commissionaire who had perceived what was happening. With the force of a second-row forward he swept about a dozen of them in two massive arms and delivered them within reach of the mike. What is more he held them there until we went back to the studio and stood by to do the same the next time they handed over to me.

At one Royal Show, in the days before it settled at Stoneleigh and was still visiting a different part of the country each year, I had allowed myself to be pressed by a colleague into taking part in a live OB he was producing. I was to wander the showground accompanied by an engineer with a mobile transmitter strapped to his back and interview interesting people 'at random'. The producer was one of those who liked things to go according to plan and so we had spent an hour or two, not rehearsing interviews – those were to be spontaneous – but checking that we could get a signal back from three selected spots in the showground. The machine we were using was called a Storno and had a reputation for being temperamental. Things had not got off to a good start. The first time they came over to me I talked to a standholder who seized the opportunity to advertise his wares in minute detail, complete with trade names and prices, and a policeman who explained to me that under police regulations he would have to fill in a special form and have it countersigned by his boss before he could be interviewed by the BBC. I was keen to make a better go of the next piece. We took up our position at the pre-arranged spot and I sorted out one or two likely interviewees when I heard on my headphones the voice of the presenter. Much had been made of the 'mystery' part of my contribution. No one was supposed to know where I would be reporting from next, including the presenter.

'And now we go over to our roving reporter, Tony Parkin, who's out there somewhere on the showground, although I've no idea where. Are you there, Tony?'

I started my piece but had not been going long when I heard our presenter saying: 'Well, I don't know what's happened to our roving reporter, we don't seem to be able to make contact at the moment.' I began all over again, but to no avail, and then after a couple more cris de cœur from the mobile studio I heard our presenter say over the air in desperation: 'Well, I've no idea what's happened to Tony Parkin. He's supposed to be at the Strawberry Fair. That's what we arranged.' The machine failed to function at all on the third occasion. Perhaps it was just as well.

Although there was a hiccup or two on most of these show OBs, by and large they went off smoothly and seemed to give a lot of pleasure to the folk who were not able to visit them personally but only hear them reported at second hand over the radio. The programmes which literally made me go grey before I was forty were the live OBs we used to do from farms and other establishments at ten past seven on a Saturday morning. Whether it was because they took place earlier in the day, whether it was because they were more ambitious or whether it was because they were always happening way off the beaten track I do not know, but they certainly gave me some worrying moments.

The idea of these programmes – and we did not do them every week; once a month was more the pattern – was to cash in on the vital asset which we had and which most other programmes lacked—the farm itself. Even at ten past seven on a Saturday morning (*what* time did you say?) it was always pulsing. Cows were being milked, pigs fed, tractors fuelled, corn ground, calves bucketed, sheep checked—not just for our benefit but as a matter of course. Decisions were being made as to whether this field was fit to drill or that one ready to harvest; whether it was too frosty to turn the cows out or whether the ram was doing his job properly. No two farms were alike and today was different from yesterday. It is this which marks farming out as distinct from most manufacturing industry and makes it so productive of material for programmes.

We developed these OBs to such a pitch that when everything went well the exhilaration was beyond belief, but when it did not the whole programme was jeopardised. The usual plan was to have about six locations—three done from the Land Rover equipped with transmitters and three from mikes laid out on cables around the buildings. I usually stayed with the OB van and acted as anchor man, aiming to have someone with me to talk to if anything went wrong. David Richardson and another farmer, David Butler from Hampshire, were my usual accomplices; they were both highly dependable broadcasters and without their professionalism and, at times, sixth sense we should have come unstuck more often than we did. So on a typical day I would open the programme and have a word or two with the farmer, before handing over to Butler who is in the milking parlour waiting to talk to the cowman. Meanwhile the farmer has joined Richardson in the Land Rover and taken him to look at some barley which is suffering from mildew where they are joined by an expert from a chemical company. Back to me for a quick chat in the yard with the daughter who cannot make up her mind whether to go to agricultural college or not before I hand over to Butler at his second location, a huge new tractor just purchased. He talks to the chap who has been driving it about its pros and cons before handing over to Richardson who has moved on in the Land Rover with the farmer to see a bunch of ewes and lambs and talk to the shepherd. While this has been going on I have gone, with microphone, into the kitchen to talk to the farmer's wife and then hand over to Butler who is with the son and their vet in the piggery discussing a disease which is threatening the herd. Richardson, meantime, has travelled to his last location, a field of sugar beet which is slow to germinate. By the time he hands back to me in the yard, I have been joined by Butler and the farmer's son for the wind-up.

Marvellous when it goes according to plan; potential chaos when it does not. Timing is absolutely crucial; everyone knows exactly how long his piece at each stage is expected to run and it must not go on for four and a half minutes if only three have been allowed, however well it is going. But stop-watches can let you down, water can get into cable junctions, cattle can knock microphones over, Land Rovers can get punctures, apart from the 'technical hitches' which are always hovering. The worst thing which could happen was a late start – an inability to make contact through the GPO line which always had to be specially laid on – and those dreaded words from the announcer in London 'We seem to be having trouble going over to the *On Your Farm* team so we'll play you . . .' All the carefully worked out timings going to pot and me anchored to the OB vehicle and incapable of contacting either of the Davids to revise the timings.

Then there was the occasion, at Sir Henry Plumb's farm in Warwickshire, when the Land Rover carrying our host and one of the Davids hit an overhanging branch which swept off the aerial, effectively cutting off all contact. The other David was en route between two of his locations and I was left in the yard with no one to talk to—except an extremely reluctant John Plumb, then still at school and not too keen to come within range of my mike.

One of the few occasions when I have ever known David Butler at a loss for words was after he caught his foot in the lead to his check-set as he got out of the Land Rover at another farm. The only way in which whoever was with the Land Rover knew when to start his interviews was by listening to a transistor radio playing the actual programme. So when he unwittingly pulled the plug from his check-set to his headphones he cut himself off from Richardson, me and the programme. To fill in the two or three minutes it took David Richardson to move to his next location I had to talk to the farmer's wife—again. The trouble was that it had been hard going the first time; we had been chatting about the difficulties of catering for a large and often unpredictable number of mouths on the farm. I do not think I shall ever forget the look of sheer horror on her face as she saw me approaching her again, microphone in hand. We were halfway through getting her to explain exactly how she cooked the bacon – and had reached the stage of discussing whether she cut the rinds off or left them on – when David Butler came back on the air. We were both relieved.

We used to take awful liberties with our hosts' forbearance. I can only remember getting my well-deserved come-uppance over the air once. We were doing one of these early-morning live OBs from David Richardson's own farm which he ran in partnership with his father and brother in Norfolk. I had persuaded Mr Richardson to bring a bunch of store cattle up into a little paddock near the buildings because this was the only way we could possibly get a microphone near them and we needed them as a focus for some chat. I picked up the mike and as an opening shot said jokingly to David's father: 'Nice bunch of cattle, but nothing special about the pasture is there?' or something like that.

To my utter amazement, and the listeners' evident amusement, he bounced back: 'Well, you told me to bring 'em up here last night for the programme. Don't you remember?' He was a wonderful, rounded man with a great sense of humour and I think I detected just a flicker of a twinkle in his eye as he affected indignation.

A series I once did and have often wished I could repeat took the form of eight monthly visits to the same farm. Again it was done in the form of a live OB, but at Wednesday lunchtime. The farm was the 1,200 acres then farmed by Nancibel Gregory and her sister on the edge of the Cotswolds near Chipping Norton. Miss Gregory was a natural broadcaster—one of those characters, and they are comparatively few, whose charisma travelled through the ether and projected itself out of the loudspeaker. I know she was good because people were always asking me about her and that is an acid test. Tom Parker, of Hampshire, was another and Bill Sinnett from Worcestershire a third. Of course there are and have been others but these three share that ability to go straight to the heart of the matter and in a way which impinges their character on the listener.

Nancibel Gregory's farming skill was legendary; she had taken over the place, then only 400 acres, at the age of nineteen on the death of her father and had, to all intents and purposes, married the farm. Her other love was horses and hunting, as I discovered the first time I went to discuss the series. We were sitting planning the opening programme when she suddenly spotted the foxhounds on the horizon. Within five minutes we were out with the Heythrop in the Land Rover, and sorting out the series had to wait until the hunt had moved on. She would have seen nothing odd about this; it was simply a question of priorities. Farming and horses came first and BBC programmes had to give way. I came across her one day at a meeting in London looking somewhat disturbed. I asked her how things were and she replied:

'Not too good. Our blacksmith was knocked down in that fog on Monday.'

'Oh, how awful,' I ventured.

'Yes,' she said, 'you can't get a horse shod. Some people have had no hunting all week.'

But that story, although true, by no means tells you everything about Nancibel Gregory. She was a compassionate woman who no doubt had already visited the blacksmith in hospital and his wife.

I remember her determination, for example, that all the chaps on her farm should have a chance to take part in the series of OBs and my concern over one of them who had a bad stammer. I just could not see how we could include him without embarrassing him and also hazarding the programme. She was equally resolute that we should. And of course, she had her way—but not until we were preparing the fifth programme at the beginning of June. I cannot remember the chap's name, but I will call him Ben.

'Now, you've got to use Ben in this one,' she insisted. 'I've had a good idea. He'll be shearing and if he dries up it'll all be drowned by the noise of the engine.'

So at lunchtime, with the programme on the air, I found myself in the woolshed sticking my mike under the nose of someone out of whom I had so far managed to elicit no more than the odd monosyllable.

'How do you like shearing?'

He turned towards me and, without a trace of a stammer, said very clearly: 'Dirty, rotten, stinking, bloody job.' And we were away.

We started the series in February 1963, driving through eight feet of snow piled each side of the lane to reach the isolated farm, and we finished at the end of October. It was so cold as we got ready for the first programme that I thought I would have difficulty in making my lips work.

Mike Soper, of Oxford University Department of Agriculture and Oxford Farming Conference fame, joined me as co-interviewer and each time we would invite another farmer from a different part of the country to discuss Miss Gregory's farming methods with her. There would also be ad hoc visitors: on one occasion we had Captain Ronnie Wallace, then Master of the Heythrop Foxhounds, and on another a wool grader. A corn merchant joined us at harvest time and, when Miss Gregory was busy sending off fat lambs, we had the buyer from the local abattoir to talk to her as she drew them out. It was a classic example of first things first. He wanted to get them loaded as they had to be slaughtered and sent off to France that day. I wanted the selection actually to be done over the air and Nancibel wanted the best deal she could get for the lambs. In the end, we agreed to draw the lambs out before the programme so as not to hold them up but to appear to come in on the tail end of this during the programme. Just as we were about to go on the air – and anyone who has ever produced or presented a live programme knows how one is feeling at that moment – the chap began to load the lambs. This drew forth an almighty roar of protest from Nancibel.

'Hey, don't you let him load those lambs. We haven't fixed a price yet.' There was no way that she was going to let us stand in the way of a good deal and she knew that once the lambs were in the lorry they could well be worth a halfpenny a pound less.

A regular contributor to these programmes was Nancibel's nephew, Richard Sumner, now well known in show-jumping circles. Every time we did a programme, Nancibel sent him off to smarten himself up. He used to protest, quite reasonably in my view, that as it was radio and not television it really did not matter if he had dirty trousers or untidy hair. But when Nancibel Gregory had made up her mind about something she usually got her way and Richard would disappear and then get his own back by not returning until frighteningly near transmission.

There was certainly never a dull moment when you were involved in producing and presenting live OBs. But they made heavy demands on your nervous energy. You would not get obese on a diet of OBs.

We do not do them so often these days but they retain their ability to make the adrenalin flow. Not long ago we planned a comparatively simple one from the Golden Jubilee meeting of the National Federation of Young Farmers' Clubs in Blackpool. My main anxiety lay in making sure that the contributors would be on parade at 6.45 a.m. when most of them were still dancing at 3 a.m. To minimise the risk we had set up a makeshift studio in the hotel where they were all staying. Then, when I had got the whole programme set up we heard that because of the Falklands crisis *On Your Farm* would be ten minutes shorter than usual. With a half-hour programme planned I would not have worried if one or two overslept. They all turned up.

THREE

Living With Listeners

Parents, said the exasperated headmaster of my son's prep school, as he watched two of them disappearing across the cricket field, are the worst possible people to have children. Leafing through the thousands and thousands of letters received in the *On Your Farm* office over the last ten years or so there were times when I felt that listeners were the worst possible people to have radio sets. Yet where would either of us be without our clientele? Anyway, they are not that bad. In fact, I rather like them, especially when they write eulogistically.

Listener reaction – favourable or unfavourable – is the very lifeblood of a producer. His programme disappears down a cable in the corner of the studio and without some sort of feedback from the audience he is tempted to feel it might just as well never have existed. So he learns to live with the letters from those who 'only heard half the programme' and so missed the point or did not hear it at all and were misinformed as to its contents by someone else. He accepts accusations of sins he feels he has not committed, or the demands that he tackle a subject on which he dwelt at length the week before last . . . and is pleased that his efforts have evoked some response. Among the negative reaction will be a letter or telephone call which will, by responding to a challenge thrown out in the programme, make it all seem worth while. Or a bit of much-appreciated praise from a totally unexpected source such as the card I received from a Norwegian living in Stavangar saying 'We truly enjoyed your programme last Saturday on the socialised farming in Norway; it was a very thorough and well-done presentation.'

It is a very time-consuming job dealing with listeners but I always tell people who are taking part in my programmes that radio is not good at putting over a lot of statistics and that they must not be upset if every 'i' is not dotted or 't' crossed, but that what radio *is* good at is making people think. If you spend your time trying to make people think you must not be surprised if some of them make counter-demands. So I do try to give a decent reply to everyone who writes, even if they sometimes have to wait a while. I blushed to see, thumbing through the files, how many of my letters started with apologies for the delay in replying. I was severely rapped over the knuckles many years ago when after a particularly large postbag my secretary sent out a postcard saying 'The Producer of On Your Farm thanks you for your letter which he has read with interest.' One recipient readdressed the card to our office and scrawled across it, 'but not sufficient interest apparently to justify the courtesy of a proper reply.' I then had to write and explain that I had received twenty letters that morning and to have given each of them a detailed answer would have taken four hours. I just could not afford to spend half my time answering letters and I felt it preferable to send out a formal acknowledgment rather than an ill-considered reply. But it made me think and put myself in the position of someone who had been so moved or stimulated by something he or she had heard over the air as to reach for pen and paper and make a trip to the post box. I resolved, wherever possible, to answer such letters personally. After all, a letter from someone who has heard a programme is about the finest compliment a producer can be paid.

Colleagues, some of whom adopt a more casual approach to letters and telephone calls, tell me that I am over-conscientious and I must say, having reviewed past correspondence, that I do seem to have been running a one-man advisory service for the last twenty years or so. It is partly because of my long-standing association with the programme which has led to the build-up of a dialogue between producer and listeners many of whom are old friends, although I have never met them, and upon whose judgment I have come to rely. A rebuke from some of them would wound badly. There is also the tendency to treat the BBC as a kind of unofficial Ombudsman: they have tried the Council and they have written to their MP without getting anywhere about the by-pass or the silage smell or their neighbour's tree-felling—why not try *On Your Farm*? This was most noticeable during the terrible foot-and-mouth outbreak of 1967–8. People would telephone me at all times of day and night to seek help; anything from simple enquiries such as whether Hereford market was open the following day to a report that a load of skins had just been driven through the village accompanied by the request that we do something to stop it. It nearly caused a divorce in my household. We had a hungry baby which needed feeding twice every night; just as my wife had got it off to sleep again and all was quiet the telephone would go. It was a farmer perhaps reporting that a local man who was helping with the disposal of cattle near Oswestry was coming home unofficially every night and driving through their yard, possibly bringing infection with him. It was an exhausting but at the same time fulfilling period for someone in broadcasting.

What sort of people write to us? It might be easier to list the sort of people who do not. Farmers, farm workers, landowners and other members of the agricultural community, of course, but an incredibly wide range of folk with nothing to do with farming who often go out of their way to divulge their profession. A lot of churchmen listen regularly (after all the Archbishop of Canterbury used to keep pigs) and I recall a Bishop of Worcester telling me that he had just come from a confirmation where he had used as a text for his address a quotation from last Saturday's *On Your Farm*. 'And do you know,' he added, 'none of the little beggars had heard the programme.' MPs find it a useful way to keep their finger on the agricultural pulse and Labour's Tam Dalyell and Conservative's Sir Paul Hawkins are among our regular correspondents. A lot of doctors seem to listen, judging from letters; so do captains of industry, some of whom start their letters somewhat irritatingly, 'It has been brought to my attention that in a programme last Saturday . . .' We seem to have a fair support from the arts. Yehudi Menuhin claims to listen and Lord Miles, the actor, rang up once with a suggestion for a future programme. We have heard from lawyers (normally in their private capacity), accountants, engineers, teachers (especially geography), peers (a 4th earl writes thought-provokingly two or three times a year) and housewives by the dozen. Our oldest letter-writer claimed to be over ninety and our youngest only nine. We receive letters not only from all over the United Kingdom and Eire but, increasingly since Radio 4 went onto 1500 metres, from further afield including Spain, Holland, France, Norway, Belgium and Denmark. It was an odd experience, having broadcast a programme recorded with a French farmer near Limoges, to have a letter from a Parisian who wanted more information on something the farmer had mentioned to do with French agriculture.

We receive a disproportionate number of letters from people in hospital, not because the programme is specially aimed at them but simply because they get woken up early.

What do they write about, all these people? Most letters are simply asking for information, some are commenting on programmes, others make suggestions for future subjects. A few correspondents simply want to let their hair down and there is an element of catharsis in some letters. A number want specific advice while others use us as an agency for finding lost friends ('Was the Mr Robinson you were talking to last Saturday the one I was at school with at Middle Wallop in 1945?'), or as a letter-forwarding service. I would not regard any of these as improper reactions to the programme, but let us have a look at some of the common subjects of correspondence in more detail.

INFORMATION Everything from names of machines referred to in the programme to authors and publishers of books. A reference last year to a farmer who had invented a packer for hay or straw bales brought letters and telephone calls from eight firms interested in manufacturing it. A lot of enquiries are for addresses of people who have taken part in programmes; listeners want to get in touch sometimes for commercial reasons and sometimes purely for interest. The BBC's policy is normally not to divulge the addresses of its contributors but in a programme like *On Your Farm* this has to be interpreted sensibly. Many of those who take part in our programmes have no objection to their addresses being revealed; some can be approached through organisations in which they hold some office—the Country Landowners' Association or the Potato Marketing Board, for example; the whereabouts of others have already been publicised in the programme. If we are in any doubt we give them a ring; otherwise we suggest that letters are sent to our office for forwarding.

REPEATS One of the most constant demands over the years has been for a repeat of *On Your Farm*. 'For so many people,' to quote a typical letter, 'this is the one morning of the week when they do not have to get up so early and it is maddening to miss your programme when so much drivel is repeated!' The writer wanted it repeated 'later in the week' by which she must have meant the following week. Here, from a producer's point of view, looms trouble. You cannot repeat a programme like *On Your Farm* in the same way as you could, say, *My Word*. It is tailored for early-morning listening and, what is more, for the specific Saturday it goes out. Put it out again the following Wednesday afternoon and it would almost certainly have to be reintroduced, and the temptation to up-date parts of it would be overwhelming. With too long a gap between the origination and the repeat I should end up doing two programmes a week, as often happened in the days when it was repeated on a regional basis at Wednesday lunchtime. Of course, every producer would like his work repeated—at an appropriate time. I tell all those kind folk who enquire that the matter is under review, which is perpetually true.

TRANSCRIPTS A week never goes by without a request for a transcript of either a whole programme or part of it. However, the BBC would grind to a halt if every word uttered on four or five channels were to be committed to paper, and we frequently have to disappoint. Of course there are exceptions. Some programmes are transcribed for our benefit and some for other people's: for instance, when the request comes from Buckingham Palace, as it has on several occasions, it is likely to be met, as will one from No. 10. Similarly a transcript will be made if it is obvious from the response that there is a widespread demand or a special reason. But it is not within the capability of the *On Your Farm* office (staff: one producer, one secretary) to provide transcripts of everything which we broadcast. Normally, where a transcript is not available, I offer to answer any specific questions or, where this is not enough, direct them to our special unit in London which will, under certain conditions, provide the service for a fee. What most listeners do not appreciate is that there is a difference between a broadcast and a transcript of the broadcast which can sometimes prove a pitiful and unworthy record of a highly enjoyable discussion or interview.

A relatively recent development has been the request for cassette recordings. This is altogether more difficult to deal with, bringing in as it does the matter of copyright not involved in the furnishing of a transcript. Personally I feel that the BBC could make more effort to sell tapes of its programmes to those who have heard and enjoyed them and not hide behind copyright obstacles which could be overcome. This would be marketing radio in the form in which it was conceived rather than as a lifeless transcript. The one request with which I tend to have little patience is from someone who admits that he could not be bothered to wake up in time for the programme and then writes or telephones to ask for a cassette recording.

COMPLAINTS Although farming may appear to be a simple non-contentious subject certain aspects of it these days, ranging from the Common Market to conservation, arouse strong passions and many of the complaints we receive are from listeners who feel keenly on a subject and think that their point of view has not been sufficiently well put. Sometimes, of course, they are right. We are, after all, happily still dealing with human beings in our programmes and in spite of every endeavour to achieve a balanced discussion it does not always work. One party will put his or her case better than another. But often the imbalance is in the mind of the listener. How else do you explain a spate of letters after a particularly heated debate, half of them saying that A was never given a chance and that B was allowed to trample all over him and the other half claiming that B's argument was suppressed and A allowed to get away with murder?

I try to give everyone who feels strongly enough to write on a matter of this kind a reasoned answer and assure them that the point they have made has been noted, as indeed it has.

We are often taken to task by our audience for not allowing our interviewees to have their say. From Angus came the following rebuke:

> I am an ex-farmer and I like to listen to the Saturday morning farming programmes and particularly the breakfast visits but I do wish you and David Richardson would SHUT UP when you have thrown out your question; do please let the people answer and don't talk over the top of them or interrupt them to jump onto something else. Don't you listen to tapes of your interviews? On Saturday I couldn't hear what your host was saying for you two yattering all the time.

The trouble is that unless we do interrupt them sometimes the whole programme would end up dealing with only one or two points—and those the ones our interviewees want to talk about, which is not always what our listeners want to hear. Of course, there has to be a balance but our subjects for this particular series, with which I will deal in detail later, are not chosen for their reticence and half an hour can pass very quickly. It is our job to structure a programme which will interest the maximum number of listeners, and the fact that these editions are particularly well received and our hosts almost invariably pleased with them shows that most of our interruptions are reasonably well concealed.

But for one complainant's Roland there is often another listener's Oliver. Consider the following:

> I must protest at the insolent manner of your Mr Anthony Parkin 'On Your Farm' this morning. He referred to us (and I am one of) farmers as 1. Blokes, 2. Clever Cocks, 3. Fly Boys, 4. Using Christian names freely.
>
> Clearly this man has not taken advantage of his parents' upbringing and neglected to make the best of the education afforded to him and is very much in need of considerable briefing before he is let loose again in such a manner that he can again be vulgar and offensive. I trust this will be arranged.

This does not sound like me, particularly as I am rather against indiscriminate use of Christian names, and 'Clever

Cocks' is not one of my normal terms of affection. Then we get, in respect of another interview done by the same person:

> Her replies to your questions came over with an integrity and feeling rarely experienced in our world of today. I believe that this interview was unique and, so rarely these days, the BBC interviewer exhibited both sympathy and sufficient time in which to phrase her replies.

While making arrangements to have that set up in Jumbo type and framed, the following arrived from 'Delighted' of Rickmansworth:

> As a regular listener to On Your Farm I was fascinated to hear Anthony Parkin so well and truly 'sewn up' by Mr Woolley this morning. The answers to the impertinent questions were first class.

With listeners like that, who needs enemies?

FOOD Since farming is about producing food and everyone who listens to *On Your Farm* is a consumer it is not surprising that food features in many of the letters we receive. Most of them come from the non-farming consumers who often find difficulty in relating what they hear on the programme to what they find on their plates. So an interview with a progressive dairy farmer about exciting advances in milk production will provoke someone into writing at length about how awful pasteurised milk tastes. An enthusiastic pig farmer explaining how he has managed to lop ten days off the normal period for getting a baconer off to the factory will incite a listener into asking where he can buy decent bacon—it is all too fat, too lean, too salty, unsmoked, watery or in some way grossly inferior to what he used to be able to buy.

Sometimes it is a question of marketing or distribution. An indignant listener hears a fruit farmer explaining that he is grubbing half his apples due to lack of demand and writes:

> I have not been able to buy *one* of those delicious English apples during the past two months and was mystified to hear on the radio *On Your Farm* that apples were being over-produced and trees were being 'scrubbed out'.

It is possible to do some good by forwarding a copy of a letter like this to, in this case, the Apple and Pear Development Council.

Just occasionally it is possible to enjoy a spot of harmless fun by scoring off someone who has written in to complain, as happened when we were strongly attacked for allowing a contributor to one of our programmes to refer in other than defamatory terms to Danish bacon and Normandy butter. 'I have nothing to do with the bacon business nor am I a farmer,' he wrote, 'but just one who buys British whenever he can. I object to a public organisation giving free advertising to *our* opposition. My corn flakes nearly choked me.' While acknowledging his indignation I could not resist suggesting that he should have been eating one of the cereals made from home-grown wheat rather than from American maize.

SIGNATURE TUNE I was obliged by my bosses to adopt the name of the old farming programme for the South-East, *On Your Farm*, for the new Saturday morning network production in 1964. So I retaliated by carrying over the signature tune of the Midland Region programme I had been producing. We have used it ever since in spite of periodic requests, nay demands, for something more in keeping with the majesty of Britain's biggest industry whose current output is valued at ten thousand million pounds. My feeling is that it is more important that a signature tune should be readily identified and associated with the programme it introduces than that it should symbolise the contents of the programme. Recently, in a spot of New Year fun, we put it to the vote of our audience and received an almost unanimous endorsement for its retention. For the record, not that it is likely to ward off further enquiries, 'The Ploughboy' was composed by William Shields (1748–1829) for his opera *The Farmer* and more recently popularised by Benjamin Britten's arrangement which was recorded with Peter Pears. So, although our Saturday programme may not yet have quite reached its thousandth edition, 'The Ploughboy' has been used in *On Your Farm* and *A Living from the Land* perhaps twelve or thirteen hundred times. A farmer's daughter living in Earls Court, London, wrote pointing out that the words rendered it totally unsuitable for a farming programme. It is the tale of a ploughboy who has moved up in the world by becoming a footman and has delusions of approaching grandeur. 'I think too many are leaving the land already,' she commented.

After the celebration of the 500th *On Your Farm* in 1974 a musician in Somerset wrote to point out a tiny flaw at the end of the tune in the flautist's final flourish. I consulted Peter Haysom Craddy who arranged and, as our music producer in Birmingham at the time, recorded the piece for us in the early sixties. He confirmed our critic's point. I must say that by the time we come to that stage of a programme I am far too relieved to think that it is over to be looking for a missing A. However, as I told our musical friend, it is good to know that we have such a critical audience.

A listener from Watford had a far more important criticism, however. She wrote:

> My Pekingese, Tula, goes nearly mad with distressed excitement each time the signature tune for *On Your Farm* is played, though she listens tranquilly to all other radio programmes. Will you please change it?

We mentioned the letter in the programme and a wag wrote saying that it was not the signature tune which caused the dog to howl but the prospect of what followed it.

NOSTALGIA The easiest short-term route to popularity in a programme is to exploit the thick vein of nostalgia which runs through agriculture. For that very reason I try to avoid it being absolutely certain that *On Your Farm* would not have survived twenty years if it had pandered to the craving too often. That does not prevent many of our listeners from writing to us on the slightest pretext to share their memories with us. The following, written in the most beautiful copperplate handwriting from an address in Coventry, is typical although a great deal shorter than some which go on for eight or nine pages:

> I left school at 13 yrs of age, I had to, to start work on a farm to help my mother have a bit more to spend on keeping all of us.

> I wouldn't care for farm work as it is carried on now. I shouldn't get the same satisfaction out of it, especially at hay-making and harvest time, cocking the hay up in rows ready for the cart horses coming along with the waggons to be loaded and with skill even at that. Putting the sheave in Shucks at harvest, and the thistles one could get in one's hands, especially with the short barley sheaves if the fields was very bad for that.
>
> When the men had to cut a road round the field so that the binder could get going, I remember how disappointed we all were if by any chance the field could not be finished the same day, because usually there would be some rabbits in it which would be too frightened usually to escape until nearly the last swawth but would all be gone during the night so we couldn't use our sticks to kill one or two to take home. Hope you'll be interested in this.

I was, especially as I can remember those days from personal experience. They say, scratch an Englishman and you find a countryman. I picture the writer, living now in retirement with one of his children, perhaps, listening to someone in *On Your Farm* talking about baled silage and letting his thoughts drift back to his own days on the farm, and then deciding to share his memories with that bloke at the BBC.

ANIMAL WELFARE A regular subject for letters in spite of the National Farmers' Union's attempts to persuade the public that there is nothing wrong with intensive farming. I know, sometimes, the moment that the words are out of one of our contributors' mouths that we are in for an avalanche of letters. It happened when Magnus Pyke talked in his exaggerated manner of injecting chickens 'in their dying throes' with something to improve the flavour. And sure enough the letters arrived:

> It is common knowledge that any product of these ghastly intensive systems is tasteless and practically uneatable, but whose fault is that? And have not these poor creatures suffered enough in their short lives without adding to the misery of their death? It is high time the Government took action against the ever increasing cruelty used in the production of cheap food for

> the masses who are either ignorant of the methods used or couldn't care less. Let them only subsidise the farmer who provides healthy food produced humanely.

I suppose a cynic would say that such a farmer would need a subsidy since he would be unable to sell his produce competitively. At least we were able, after consulting Dr Pyke, to assure our correspondent that the injection was not given until after the bird was dead. Our programme, apparently, is not always well-timed. A Herefordshire housewife, with a sense of humour, wrote as follows:

> I enjoy listening to *On Your Farm* but guess what I was eating for my breakfast when you were talking to that pig producer in Ireland—yes, bacon. It was at the precise moment when he said he fed them with blood from the abattoir for extra protein. Somehow the two don't mix too well and my bacon became very unappetising! I think I'll try beef sausages or steak next Saturday and see what happens.

I was careful not to include in the following week's programme anything about the feeding of dried poultry manure to cattle.

EMPLOYMENT I sometimes think that we should re-name our office the On Your Farm Job Centre. We seem to attract a large number of enquiries in the course of a year, mostly from the parents of young people who want to get into farming. Many are having difficulty in finding the necessary pre-college year on a farm and I have thought once or twice of setting up a bureau through the programme but there would probably be thousands of youngsters wanting jobs and hardly any farmers offering them. I usually put them in touch with their local youth employment officer and their nearest County Agricultural College and suggest that the best way of getting pre-college employment is the time-honoured one of getting on a bike. A farmer is much more likely to take on someone who has been hanging round the yard at weekends making himself useful than an unknown quantity who applies by letter. If the youngster happens to live in Wandsworth of course it is more difficult, but not impossible.

Some of our listeners make much heavier demands when they ask for specific advice regarding their offspring. I thought I had been fairly generous in devoting time and thought to helping a dentist from the Home Counties with suggestions for his daughter. Imagine my surprise when, about three years later, I received a further letter from him. 'You may remember advising me about my daughter Anthea who, as a result, is now reading bio-chemistry at Nottingham and hopes to graduate next year. I write now about my son, William . . .'

LABOUR This is guaranteed to raise the hackles of our audience whenever it is mentioned. Indeed, many of our farmers seem to wish that it never was mentioned, including one of our most loyal listeners who described a programme put out four or five years ago when farm workers were parading in the streets of London as one of the most disgraceful he had ever heard and calculated to cause revolution.

The general reaction among farmers to any discussion about labour is that it is irresponsible to discuss it, while that of farm workers is that we are pussy-footing around the issue. When a Herefordshire farmer in one of our 'Fieldspace' slots (where we invited people to let their hair down on a subject of their choice) pleaded with his fellow farmers to give their workers a better deal I was attacked in a letter from a farmer in Northamptonshire for making farm workers dissatisfied. A farm manager from Essex on another occasion wrote:

> The reason for many of our men being paid the minimum or near minimum wages is that we do not farm well enough. Poor farming pays poor wages. Good farming pays everyone, Boss, men and country.

It is a subject which I would willingly steer clear of but feel that I would be failing in my duty if I did. Let us leave the last word on the subject with the widow of a lifetime farm worker who told us, following a programme about tied cottages in 1974, that she always listened to *On Your Farm*:

> I feel that it's time someone spoke up for the good employers who do not turn out their employees unnecessarily. In our case my husband was ill for almost 10 years and although we

> accepted the fact that we could not expect our employer to pay us anything we were allowed to occupy our bungalow to the end of his life. Our local council knew of our circumstances and in due course allotted me a bed-sitter, for which I am truly grateful.

WOMEN This is a subject guaranteed to cause an outburst of letter writing whenever it is – or is not – mentioned. If the female sex is referred to in *On Your Farm* we are accused of saying the wrong things by Ms. This or Ms. That and if we do not bring women into the programme we are condemned for ignoring them. We have been reported to the Equal Opportunities Commission but so far have suffered no injury.

The ingenuity displayed in finding male chauvinist attitudes in the programme never ceases to astonish me. In describing a farm which had succumbed to the seduction of the computer I had referred to the secretary who operated it as 'middle-aged'. This was a simple way of pointing out that you did not necessarily have to be young to come to terms with computers, and at the same time I was paying tribute to her versatility. But no, it was all part of the *On Your Farm* plot to put women down: the remark to one listener at least was 'quite irrevelant':

> I pricked up my ears and waited through the whole programme for you to refer to other people's ages such as 'a middle-aged cowman', a 'middle-aged farmer' or even a 'middle-aged dairy farmer'. Not even a 'middle-aged cow'. There was no reference to any man's age at all or any animal. Why was the secretary who operated the computer singled out for her age reference? Was it because it was a woman? By the way you are probably middle-aged (by your voice) but you do not say, when you come on the air 'Good morning, this is your middle-aged announcer.'

Farming, in my opinion, will continue to remain a largely male-dominated industry where the woman's role, with certain very important exceptions, will be the vital one of the farmer's wife—cooking meals, drying clothes, bringing up the next generation of farmers, answering the telephone, fetching spares rather than humping fertiliser bags and pitching bales.

I do not see a large increase in the number of women employed unless we reach the next logical step in the process which is a law requiring a proportion of the workforce to be female. To prove that I am not entirely alone, let me quote from a letter received from a nurse who had heard a report in *On Your Farm* on equal pay in farming:

> As a member of the Women's Land Army for 4½ years during the War, I would like to state very firmly that my own physical strength was only about two-thirds of that of the men with whom I worked, and this was cause of continual frustration to me and led to my frequently overtaxing myself to try and 'keep up' with them (although they often chivalrously slowed down for my benefit).
>
> I was given especially selected jobs out in the fields but the bulk of my time was spent milking cows, rearing calves and keeping cowsheds clean which I could just about manage.
>
> When the new law takes effect, farmers will I am sure opt to employ a man every time, if one is available, unless the job to be done is actually more suitable for a woman—and what job on a farm could be that?

She signed off, 'Sincerely in no desire to be equal with men in all things.' As a responsible producer I shall continue to try and hold the ring fairly between those who object to having to advertise for a pigperson when what they want is a pigman who can lift the hundredweight concrete slab in the yard on his own when the drain gets blocked and those who want to see at least half our sugar beet harvesters driven by women.

ORGANIC FARMING Any mention of farming without the use of chemicals is sure to bring in the letters. Indeed any failure to mention it is also guaranteed to have the same effect. In my experience the organic farming lobby is better at writing about it than actually doing it. We have broadcast a number of programmes with commercially successful exponents of so-called muck and mystery farming. But I think that all of them would admit that their profitability lies in their ability to obtain a substantial premium for their produce because it is grown without the help of fertilisers and sprays. The fact that more of them are not doing it suggests that the organic food market is limited.

The question I always put to those who write and ask why we do not feature more organic farmers is 'Who are they? You tell me the name and address of anyone who has been farming successfully without chemicals over a long period and making a profit and we will go and see him.' After all, I once sent an interviewer on a costly 300-mile trip to see a fruit-grower in Essex who managed without sprays. Everyone likes to hear of a farmer who can make a good living without chemicals but the absence of any sizeable body of them, apart from the few who are cashing in on the health food market, suggests that it is not as easy as it looks. Mind you, more research might help but you are not likely to find ICI or May and Baker financing it. Or any of the other fertiliser or agro-chemical firms.

REGULARS The range of subject matter covered by the *On Your Farm* mail bag never ceases to astonish me. What other programme could, by the same post, attract from Scotland a saying attributed to Horace and from Lincoln a cri de cœur about a parrot?

There are, as I have said, a number of our listeners whom I count as old friends who monitor the output in a civilised way and comment by letter from time to time. Many of them I have never met but one whom I have is Lewis Stewart who practises what he preaches on a small farm near Stirling and it was he who quoted the Horace. 'Naturam expellas furca, tamen usque recurret', which means 'you can drive out Nature with a fork but it will return again'. Horace may well have been alluding to the sure way in which bindweed will show up in your garden once you think you have got rid of it but Lewis was using the quotation in its much wider sense as a warning about certain aspects of modern agriculture which are trying to stand Nature on its head. What sparked the letter off was a light-hearted piece by Michael Clark about progressive dairy farming:

> Mr Clark mentioned in the licensed way broadcasters are allowed that he did not know how the cow survived under wild

> conditions. One of Nature's wonders, the rumen, was developed through the rigours of natural selection. Just because a few tycoons wish to put the bovine in a straight jacket, let us not forget our modest beginning! According to the authorities the cow would graze very rapidly out on the open grassland or prairie where there was little protection and then return to the cover of, say, woodland to redigest the food in safety. The whole process was infinitely more clever than cubicles, tower silos and slurry tanks!

For years Mr Stewart used to write to me on the blank sheets of high-quality paper torn out of his VAT booklets and, as a reciprocal gesture, I used to reply on the backs of Ministry handouts. Now, they have changed the layout of the VAT booklets – 'A wee victory, perhaps!?' he asks – and his letters come on 100 per cent recycled paper. Long may he keep up the correspondence.

I cannot say I welcome so warmly the equally regular messages from a long-serving listener in the Channel Islands. Largely negative in tone his views usually appear written on a postcard with commendable economy of words. There is never any doubt what he means but I have yet to discover anything of which approves. He is against 'factory farming' and exports of live animals—any chance of their being stopped, he enquires, 'OR IS MONEY MORE IMPORTANT?' A programme with a farmer who happened to be an MFH brought a card a couple of days later (since he wastes no time in posting them) saying simply 'HUNTING, I PROTEST, TELL HIM.' An interview with a saleswoman on a stand at a show brought a quite unjustifiable attack 'THESE GIRLS—IS IT NECESSARY TO HAVE THESE TARTS ON STANDS?' He is against the Common Market and although he used to write from a farm address seems at odds with farmers—'WHAT A REACTIONARY CROWD FARMERS ARE—CONSERVATIVES, OF COURSE.' But he reserves most of his vitriol for the voices he hears. 'NO. NEVER AT ANY TIME YANK, CANADIAN OR AUSTRALIAN VOICES. PROGRAMME SPOILT SO DID NOT LISTEN.' And again, 'VOICES NOT SUITABLE FOR BROADCASTING. TRAINING NEEDED. COULD NOT UNDERSTAND SOME SPEAKERS.' However, when we included a report from a journalist with excellent if somewhat fruity English it simply brought the comment: 'KEEP THE COLONELS OFF THE AIR.' I have a picture of him sitting every Saturday morning, blood pressure rising, stamped postcard ready to hand waiting for the inevitable offence.

I must admit that I would miss his communications as I would those who repeatedly end their letters: 'I have listened to On Your Farm for the last time.'

The parrot letter arrived following another of Michael Clark's contributions—this time from the Royal Show. Among all the technical stuff we like to include a lighter element and on this occasion he had interviewed an official of the Parrot Society which was exhibiting at the event. The following Monday came a letter from a distraught parrot owner asking for the address of the society. 'I shall join immediately,' she wrote. 'My parrot's bill has become cross-hobbled and I need instant advice.' My secretary sent her the address without delay.

One April 1st, for a bit of harmless fun, we played a phoney musical request for a dairy cow during milking. The laugh was on us because the following week we received a letter addressed from 'The Cowshed', at a farm in Shropshire:

> Having had to listen to your programme for five years, us cows were very pleased to hear last week that at long last we are to have our own request programme. We also wondered if we could have Uncle David Richardson to answer our problems which we would send in by post. Many of us have no natural husband to turn to with problems, only a bowler-hatted gent who treats us worse than his car and with less sympathy.
>
> Our own problem is that our cowman must use the wrong handcream as his hands are very rough, but how can we tell him without hurting his feelings? Also during the period of your programme he often forgets to change the units over as he gets very engrossed in your discussions. So we wondered if every five minutes you would remind Tom the cowman to change the units over. Yours faithfully, Dolly (Mrs F7631–281).

I have always insisted that a sense of humour was one of the most important attributes of anyone involved in producing or presenting a programme like *On Your Farm* and it was good to see it reciprocated by our listeners. One of the cheekiest requests we have had, so impudent that but for the inevitable knock-on effects I was tempted to accede to it, came from a veterinary student:

> My dad's a potato and corn farmer near Spalding, Lincs. I know it's a bit unusual but if you have a spare 10 seconds on your programme, could you wish him a Happy Birthday on March 4, please? It's the only programme I know for sure he'd be listening to and it would give him a pleasant surprise.

I would love to have helped but we would soon have been competing with Tony Blackburn so I replied asking him whether he had thought of sending a birthday card.

INVITED LETTERS From time to time we invite letters on a specific subject, usually following a particularly provocative talk or interview, and broadcast a selection of them the following week. Although an invitation to write is always taken up and often results in some interesting material for the programme it is a statagem I resort to comparatively rarely, for a number of reasons. Letters of this kind are often written in a declamatory style and, in my view, sit uncomfortably in an informal programme like *On Your Farm*. They sound like letters, however well they are read. Not surprising, you may say, since they *are* letters, but they are not natural letters. Or the writer, knowing that there are limitations on time, has tried to cram every point into a couple of paragraphs, making the argument extremely cogently but in a manner unsuited to a radio programme. If I switch on *Woman's Hour* or *PM* I can tell immediately if I have hit the middle of listeners' letters. Of course, we are partly to blame for this by our obsession with time and our request for letters 'on a postcard, please.' Nowadays, when it costs the same to send a postcard as a letter, cards are not so common (I have a mental image of postcard firms being kept in business these days solely by people who want to write to the BBC). The reason why we ask for postcards is that there is a limit as to how much you can write on a card and, although letters now often come on writing paper, many folk have got the message and keep them brief.

Unfortunately, however, not all our letters are brief, and there lies another reason why we do not invite reactions too often. If the letters are not short and highly concentrated they are frequently long and discursive. By the time you have read the twentieth four-page letter in difficult handwriting you are beginning to wonder whether it was a good idea to ask what listeners thought. Having made your selection, as fairly as you possibly can to reflect the views expressed, you are still not out of the wood. The practice of broadcasting listeners' views is still open to question as a means of gauging opinion, according to some members of our audience, particularly when the expression of attitude does not conform with their own.

The response, on occasion, has been so rich as to form the basis for another programme. This happened a couple of years ago following a typically controversial piece from Eddie Straiton, the 'TV Vet', in which he predicted no less than the end of agricultural practice in this country within ten years. Such was the quality of the letters which followed, most of them from vets and farmers, the two parties intimately concerned, that I was able to use points from them to structure the whole of a further programme on the subject.

MISUNDERSTANDINGS Radio has many strengths but one abiding weakness which can never be overcome. It is ephemeral. As a producer one tries to minimise its imperfection in this respect but the inability, compared to, say, a newspaper, of being able to read a paragraph twice remains. So one resorts to the old adage, 'tell them you're going to tell them, then tell them, then tell them you've told them.' This is not patronising the audience in any way; it is simply being practical.

Sometimes a statement in a programme is not so much mis-heard as misunderstood. A farmer was complaining of the difficulty of giving his farm to his son because of the threat of the proposed Capital Transfer Tax. This drew a short but pertinent letter from a hopeful listener in Surrey who wrote: 'I was surprised to hear farmers can't give their farms away. Could you please let me have their addresses as I haven't seen them advertised in any of the farming papers and I should like one?'

I find that the longer I work in radio the more conscious I am of both its strengths and weaknesses. Most of the latter arise from the temporary nature of the offering coupled with the fact that not every 'listener' is listening to the exclusion of everything else. It does not surprise me to receive a letter from someone who claims never to miss an *On Your Farm* which begins 'Dear Michael Parker'. I have been addressed as Anthony Hopkins, Norman Parkinson, Michael Parkinson (but not Cecil, so far) and various permutations of David Richardson, Michael Clark and my own name. I was on a farm in Wiltshire one day interviewing two farmer neighbours whom I had never met before and, such is the nature of the game, was unlikely to meet again. Yet I can remember them both clearly, what they looked like, what they wore, the farmyard, the spot where we did the interview and what they said. So I thought it slightly undeserved when, as I was leaving one of them said to me: 'I expect you make a lot of short-term friends in this job.' I looked suitably quizzical. 'You'll have forgotten us by the time you get down the end of the lane,' he persisted. I assured him that that was not the case. 'Well, goodbye Mr Smith,' I said, holding out my hand. He seized it and held it. 'Call me Jim,' he said.

'Goodbye, Jim.' He held on to my hand and put his leathery face close to mine and murmured: 'And perhaps I might call you—Leonard?' I reckoned that was fifteen-all, if not thirty-fifteen. I have never met my ITN namesake although I did meet the one on *The Guardian*. We are unrelated and not part of a media Mafia.

Not long ago, as a tribute to a famous farmer, we repeated a programme we had done with him ten years earlier. I prefaced the repeat with about two minutes explaining that he had died at a ripe old age and a further minute at the end bemoaning his death and speculating as to how the farm would get on without him. A few days later arrived a letter from someone who said how much he had enjoyed hearing him and hoped that we should have him in the programme on a regular basis in future.

A story which I think demonstrates as well as any what a powerful medium radio can be happened some years ago. We had interviewed a young man in Cornwall who had started farming in very difficult circumstances and was succeeding by sheer determination and hard work. The interview was broadcast and the following week my secretary handed me a letter containing a cheque for enough to buy him a down-calving heifer—perhaps £600 at today's prices. It was from a woman who had been so touched by his story that she felt she wanted to help him. We passed the cheque on to an incredulous young farmer and next time I was near I called in and he showed me the cow.

So there are listeners—and listeners. But any producer who ignored the drift of letters and telephone calls would be unlikely to flourish for long and would not deserve to do so.

FOUR

Sharing Breakfast

After four years of doing live broadcasts from farms at ten past seven in the morning I had come to the conclusion that if I was going to survive to draw my pension I would have to find a different way of capitalising on the timing of the programme. Although they were extremely successful they were rapidly giving me grey hairs.

One May morning in 1969 I was driving over to the National Agricultural Centre at Stoneleigh and, as usual, thinking about programmes and, in particular, what I was going to do about one coming up in a fortnight's time which was then a total blank. Out of the blue came the idea of having breakfast with a farmer and his family and recording the conversation across the table. I did not give the concept long to crystallise; no longer than it took me to drive the seven miles or so between Droitwich where I thought of it and Feckenham where I stopped the car and telephoned Peter Smith who farms just outside Wolverhampton (and several other places as well).

'Look Peter, I've just had this idea for a new series and wondered whether you'd be prepared to act as a guinea pig.'

'Yes, I don't mind. Whatever you say.' Peter gave me the impression that if I had arranged for him to go on the next moon rocket to report on lunar agriculture the reply would have been the same. And so the famous *On Your Farm* breakfast programmes were born, the format with which the programme has since become increasingly identified. 'Oh, you're the chap who eats all those marvellous breakfasts' is a frequent gambit when I am introduced. We broadcast the first one from the Smiths' sixteenth-century farmhouse at Codsall on May 17th and we have been doing them at roughly monthly intervals ever since. We returned to the Smith family for our hundredth breakfast in November 1980 and we are now well on the way towards our second century.

In retrospect, I have to admit that the idea was probably born out of a chat I had with Tom McDowell, then chief press officer at the Ministry of Agriculture, several years earlier. He was desperate to get his Minister, Fred Peart, on *On Your Farm*. 'Have lunch with him; have dinner with him,' he pleaded. 'Have breakfast with him.' We did indeed have breakfast with him—but not for many years. Not until he had become Lord Peart in 1976, having handed over his Ministry reluctantly to John Silkin. I say reluctantly because I know he was keen to remain in office until December of that year when he would have become the longest-serving Minister ever and we had planned our breakfast with him to coincide with this. But it was not to be and we ate our bacon and eggs at The Farmers' Club in London three months early—with the new Lord Privy Seal.

But back to that first programme: Why did I choose Peter Smith for it? There are several reasons. It was partly because he was fairly near Birmingham and if it did turn out to be disastrous, we could probably cobble something else together in time for transmission; partly because it could be serviced by our OB engineers from Pebble Mill, chaps with whom I was used to working and who, I knew, would bend over backwards to make it a success technically. Partly it was because there were all the ingredients there for a good programme—successful farmer, largely self-made, with a nice wife, several children and an interesting set-up; and partly because I was almost certain that he would say yes.

Peter is one of the most dynamic men in British agriculture who has become very rich by sheer business acumen and far-sightedness. Not a man to suffer fools gladly. He once told an astonished reporter who asked him how he could justify having his own helicopter: 'I don't have to justify it. I can b—— well afford it!' When he was Chairman of the NFU Soft Fruit Committee he used to show his disdain for the establishment aspects of the Union by going skiing over the period of its AGM. He would then fly home from Zermatt for an hour or two to present his committee's report, catch the first plane back and carry on skiing. I knew that anything he said during that first breakfast would be worth listening to. And I was not disappointed.

Mind you, it nearly did not take place. As an interviewing team I had invited Stuart Seaton, editor of the *Farmers' Guardian* and Frank Taylor, a farmer from Nottinghamshire. Peter, like many successful farmers, had become very interested in what has now become known as 'conservation'. He had planted hundreds of trees round the farm and near the house had created a large lake which attracted a lot of birds. Frank arrived at the house and immediately opened the boot of his car, liberating a large Labrador which straightway started to flush all the waterfowl off Peter's lake. Many of them were nesting and it was a nasty moment. Luckily the dog was very obedient.

I set a lot of store by the two-man interview team, and for this job I particularly like a combination of a journalist and a working farmer. Having done a great deal of interviewing over the years I know how difficult it can be to listen to the answer while framing the next question without leaving awkward pauses and to keep up the flow of objective questioning. Having two minds on the job in what is in effect a live half-hour programme removes a lot of the strain; but the farmer–journalist team has another advantage. There are often technical or commercial areas where the journalist on his own might be at fault. Equally there are questions of public interest which the farmer may not think of or perhaps may prefer not to pursue. This is where the journalist comes in, representing the taxpayer, the consumer, the man in the street. The formula seems to work effectively and I have only departed from it rarely, usually on the occasions where our host has been a farm worker and I felt it inappropriate to confront him with someone who might be seen as a mouthpiece of the employers.

Now to answer the question which arises every time these *On Your Farm* breakfasts are talked about. Yes, we do actually do them at breakfast time, across the breakfast table having eaten (or sometimes still eating!) breakfast. But no, they are not live in the real sense of the term. For economy reasons we record them, usually on the Friday morning. I do try and make it as near as possible to quarter past seven but sometimes it has to be earlier or later to fit in with the farmhouse routine; cows have to be milked, children have to be got off to school and so on. I make it a golden rule never to accept an invitation to stay the night because I feel that there is a strong psychological advantage in actually knocking on someone's door at seven o'clock in the morning even though we may have had a look round the previous afternoon.

One of my secretary's jobs then is to check on three things—dogs, telephones and chiming clocks. Dogs have a habit of barking and while a little bark from a sheepdog sounds all right we have had them barking for half an hour. Or they whine and scratch at the door to be let out, and there was one occasion when I did three-quarters of the programme with a whippet sitting on my knee. In television it is very easy to interpret a noise—a crackling fire, a loud-ticking clock, a dog can all be explained by means of a quick pan or cutaway shot, and no one need say anything. In radio you have to make rather a meal of it so it is easier to shut the dog out if you can and take the telephone off the hook. There was one occasion when we were not allowed to disconnect the phone. We were having breakfast with Joe Godber shortly after he had been made Minister of Agriculture. It was the height of the Cod War and Mr Godber (as he then was) was expecting a call from Number Ten at any moment. So it was with some apprehension that I embarked on the programme, wondering whether I could incorporate the Prime Minister into it should he call and, if so, how. I was relieved when we reached the end of the recording without having to cope with Mr Heath and we were just relaxing when the telephone rang.

I raised a cheeky eyebrow to the Minister and said: 'Probably Number Ten.'

'Very likely,' he replied, and his wife went to answer it. In a few seconds she was back. The Minister was preparing to rise from his seat.

'It's Mrs Bloggs,' she said, 'to say the cat's back.'

When we visited Tony Stodart (yet another of our hosts subsequently to be ennobled!) he had such a beautiful chiming clock that I could not resist embodying it in the programme. The reason that I normally ask for them to be silenced is that, for reasons I explained earlier, it is not always possible to start the recording bang on quarter past seven and there is always some clever chap among our listeners who counts the chimes and points out that it struck eight o'clock in the middle of the programme. When this happens I simply say, 'Well, you know what these farmhouse clocks are like,' but it is easier to avoid it. Setting up the Stodarts' clock so that it would chime (on the quarters) at the right times in the programme took quite a bit of doing but it worked and we thought it worth while. Two or three days later I received a postcard with the simple message: 'A *very* nice striking clock!' It was from large-scale farmer Elizabeth Creak with whom we had recently breakfasted at her splendid house at Snitterfield in Warwickshire. The joke was that we had asked her to stop not one but three chiming clocks and one of them she still had not managed to get started again.

Some interruptions are unpredictable like the Sussex farmer's young son who obviously wanted to go to the loo in the middle of the recording. We could not understand why his parents were so loth to let him go—until they did. It was a very old house. He creaked his way upstairs, across the floor and into the bathroom which was right over the breakfast table. Then he pulled the chain which made a noise like Big Ben getting ready to strike followed by Niagara Falls.

Equally unpredictable was the knock on the door when we were breakfasting with Steve Roberts and family. It was someone calling to buy a bag of spuds and the fact that Steve insisted that his wife sold them one probably explains why he is such an effective chairman of the Milk Marketing Board. Although his wife is now Lady Roberts I am quite sure it has not stopped her selling potatoes.

Although we try to give the impression of a totally spontaneous conversation across the breakfast table, even the most naïve of our listeners must realise that there is quite a bit more to it than simply dropping in for some bacon and eggs and having a chat. I get a programme under way by visiting a prospective host, often quite a long time before the transmission, to see whether it is going to work—whether there is enough to talk about, whether they really want to do it. I make a lot of notes for the benefit of myself and my co-interviewer, especially where there are areas which may need researching before we return. Depending on the location and the time of year we usually descend on our hosts about mid-afternoon of the Thursday, the team consisting simply of myself and whoever is helping me with the interviewing, my secretary who has multifarious duties apart from dogs, clocks and telephones and our outside broadcast engineer who has a vital role to play. His job is to try and make a farmhouse kitchen sound not like a bathroom (which it often can) nor yet like a studio, but like a farmhouse kitchen. He has to rig it so that everyone including granny and six-year-old Tommy are on mike.

We have a look round if there is anything to see (by no means all of our hosts are farmers), and have a good chat around all the areas we might want to touch on in the morning, and then go to our hotel. This is where the real work starts. This is where the programme is structured. By the time we go to bed, not often much before midnight, we have a very simple typed running order. Before we go to sleep my co-interviewer and I have each fleshed this out with our own notes so that what we have to work from in the morning is a common skeleton showing the agreed structure of the programme with our individual annotations. This preserves an element of surprise between us so that although we know that we are proceeding from A to B by a main road, who knows what minor detours may be made on the way. David Richardson and I have worked together on so many of these, however, that we have developed a sixth sense which often anticipates the surprises.

Of course the last thing you really want before tackling a half-hour programme of this sort is a huge breakfast, yet our hosts each seem determined to outdo their predecessors. For some it is an everyday occasion but most of our hosts confess to having a pretty modest breakfast normally, or even not bothering. 'I wish you'd come more often,' said one farmer's son. 'It's the first decent breakfast we've had for years.' Sir Richard Trehane confided, when we went to his farm in Dorset, that his normal breakfast was a cup of black coffee and a couple of aspirins but I suspect he was pulling our legs because his wife produced the most splendid spread of local produce. Sir Richard then opened several bottles of champagne when the programme was over, establishing a precedent which has unfortunately never been followed up.

So, once a month, we celebrate the ritual of the good old English breakfast which seems to be fast disappearing. We, who at home would normally make do with a little scrambled egg or perhaps just toast and marmalade, join our hosts – who usually do much the same as us – in demolishing a bowl of porridge followed by mounds of bacon, fried eggs, sausages, mushrooms, tomatoes, fried bread, perhaps a dish of kidneys, and then heaps of toast and marmalade or honey to finish off. I am not complaining. I thoroughly enjoy it. I just, sometimes, wish that I did not have to record a programme over the closing stages and could really relax.

Occasionally there is an interesting variation. Sandy Copeland's wife, for example, served lamb chops when we visited them before he gave up running the Beaverbrook farming empire in Somerset: Sandy I should explain, comes from New Zealand. At Fraser Morrison's it was Loch Fyne kippers (I think I ate three!) as befits the Chairman of the Royal Highland and Agricultural Society. Breakfast with turkey-king Brian Dale and his wife Margaret included, appropriately, turkey sausages, and with Tom Boden in Staffordshire it was fried oatcakes, another local speciality. John Silkin's charming wife, known to my generation as Rosamund John the actress, served kedgeree when we breakfasted in their London flat only a division bell away from the House of Commons, I think to remind us that her husband was Minister of Agriculture, *Fisheries* and Food.

Only once have I failed to complete the course and that was when I was served a bad egg. Not just a little bit off but actually green. I am not going to say where, it would bring too many blushes, but the irony was that not fifty yards from the back door of the farmhouse were half a million laying hens. It was just sheer bad luck; but what was I to do? I wanted to avoid anything which might upset the programme we were about to record which was not proving to be one of the easiest. Ah well, honour of the BBC, stiff upper lip and all that: I must eat it. I tried it. Then I thought don't be stupid, you have a half-hour programme to do in five minutes' time, a programme which however good or bad will be broadcast tomorrow morning throughout the United Kingdom. So I messed the egg up a bit to make it look smaller, hid what I could under my knife and fork and made noises to the effect that although the breakfast was marvellous I could not quite manage it all. I have often wondered since whether my hosts had also seen the situation and were wondering how I was going to get out of it without mutual embarrassment, rather like my wife who once sat mesmerised as I forked into my mouth a small slug she had been watching crawl out of my lettuce; I thought it was a tasty bit of mushroom out of the omelette.

Although the programme is being recorded I like to treat it as a live show, for two reasons. One is that it is not usually practical to have a second go; and the other is that I think it keeps everyone on their toes. So, having topped up our coffee, we keep our fingers crossed and make a start, aiming to record a couple of minutes more than we need in order to edit out the odd cough or splutter.

Before we started the breakfast series, when we were still doing the programme live from a farm on a Saturday morning, it used to irritate me that listeners were reluctant to believe that we were there in the milking parlour or out in the sugar beet while they were actually hearing it. This was in spite of the fact that we often referred to the weather, one of the things which even the meteorologists cannot always predict accurately. We would say in the programme, for example: 'Well, it has been fine all week and Mr Jones started shearing his sheep on Thursday. They had a good day again yesterday, he tells me, but things don't look too promising this morning; it's raining quite hard here at the moment. What do you think, Mr Jones? Do you reckon you'll have any luck today?' Mr Jones then says something like this: 'Well, I don't know. It has been raining since I got up at half past five but they say rain before seven, fine before eleven, so we may be lucky.' Then just to ram it home, I would probably say: 'Well, it's only half past seven at the moment, so it may lift.' Within the week I would be certain to meet someone who said: 'Enjoyed your programme last

Saturday. What I can never understand is how you knew it was going to be raining when you recorded it.'

Towards the end of that particular series I got desperate. I used to say 'We really are here, you know, and if you live anywhere near Little Twittering why don't you pop over and see us?' No one ever did. But the memory of that has lived on to haunt me ever since we started the breakfast series which, as I have explained, are recorded the day before. I remember that shortly after we changed tack I took my car into the local garage one Saturday morning. The previous day we had recorded a breakfast chat with that incredible man Rex Paterson on his farm in Hampshire and it had been broadcast that morning. The chap who looked after my car was a faithful listener to *On Your Farm* and he was used to my calling in on a Saturday on the way home from doing a programme. 'Heard you this morning,' he would say. 'Where was it—Derbyshire?' and he would look at my steaming car and do a mental sum. On this Saturday morning it was about half past ten when I drove in and we are getting on for 150 miles from Hampshire. 'Good Lord,' he gasped incredulously, 'you got a move on this morning.'

Most of the *On Your Farm* breakfasts go more or less according to plan, give or take the odd child bursting into tears or postman arriving with a COD parcel. There was one when we attempted something rather ambitious—and nearly came unstuck. Our host on this occasion was Paddy Taylor and the location a house at Cricket St Thomas near Chard which has since become well known to television viewers as the big house in *To The Manor Born*. I had known Paddy for twenty years or so by the time we invited ourselves to breakfast in 1978. He was a tenant farmer in Staffordshire and one of the first really to exploit grass for milk production. But by the time we went to Cricket St Thomas he had gone with his son John into farming about a thousand acres with four dairy herds and also a wildlife park. Both Paddy and his son John were thrusters in their different ways and the delightful family, the setting and the story all betokened an outstanding programme.

There was just one difficulty. John was also managing director of a company set up to develop agriculture in the

Middle East and only a few days before we were due to do the programme had unexpectedly had to fly out to Saudi Arabia. He was a key figure in any conversation, having been the one who actually had been responsible for the move from Staffordshire. On the other hand it was too late to postpone the visit as it had already been trailed the previous Saturday. It was Paddy who came up with the answer. 'Why don't we get him on the telephone from Riyadh?' Why not, indeed. Our engineers at Pebble Mill seemed to think it could be done. The chaps from the Network Production Centre at Bristol were slightly less confident but understandably as the location lay within their area and so they were the ones who actually had to sort out the mechanics. Anyway, it seemed worth a try so, armed with a special telephone supplied by my colleagues in Birmingham, we set out for Cricket St Thomas. We talked to John in Riyadh that night and arranged for him to be in his office the following morning to take a call. Everything seemed to be in order and so, keeping our fingers firmly crossed, we sorted out the running order and went to bed.

We had arranged that, at a certain point in the programme, Mrs Taylor would leave the table and go next door to the telephone and put the call through. When she had got her son on the line she would come back and let us know. I would go first leaving David Richardson to carry on talking to the Taylors long enough to cover the time it took me to get to the telephone and make contact, after which he would join me to talk to John. Everything seemed to work like a dream. The conversation swung along with Paddy and his wife and son Stephen who was running the farming enterprise at Cricket on a day-to-day basis. About ten minutes in, I asked Mrs Taylor if she would try and get John on the telephone while we carried on talking about the cows. Sure enough, three or four minutes later she returned and announced the magic words: 'John's on the line now.'

John certainly was on the line and I spoke to John. The only trouble was that due to a gremlin somewhere in the works we just were not able to record the conversation at sufficiently high a quality to be able to use it. Which left us rather in a spot. Here we were on a Friday morning in deepest Somerset with a programme already trailed to go out the following day and built around the close inter-relation between Paddy and his son and between Cricket St Thomas and the Middle East—and no John. We had to think quickly. It was the engineer who suggested recording the telephone conversation in Bristol later on. Could John manage it? Well, he had an important appointment but could just about manage eleven-thirty to twelve, our time. So we asked him to stand by and my secretary tried desperately to contact someone in Bristol to make the necessary arrangements but of course it was much too early in the day. We were, after all, still having breakfast.

I have always found David Richardson a tower of strength in a crisis and so he proved to be on this occasion because we were a long way from being out of the wood. John Taylor might well have rearranged his day in Riyadh to be at his desk at half past eleven but we still did not know whether we could book a studio in Bristol to record the chat or whether we might for some reason be unable to make contact. Meanwhile we were only halfway through a programme which, in its present form, depended for its success on the Saudi connection. We now, in very limited time, had to do virtually two versions of the programme—one with John and one without. With the help of the notes my secretary makes we had to go back and re-record various bits of the conversation, substituting for remarks like, 'and we hope to get John on the line later on' something like, 'and it's a great pity John can't be here to talk about the Middle East operation.' We had to record a new version of the middle section where I asked Mrs Taylor to try and get John on the line, including the ensuing conversation which would have had her footsteps over it, and we also had to record a fresh lot of footsteps for the return from the telephone of David and myself in case it all worked out. We then had to record the rest of the programme including an extra ten minutes in case we failed to get John's contribution and two versions of the wind-up, one referring to the Riyadh telephone call and one regretting John's absence. In retrospect a wiser and certainly far easier solution would have been to leave things as they were and carry on the programme where we left off, simply getting Mrs Taylor to say 'I'm sorry, I can't get through to him.'

All this, of course, took a lot of time and it was turned ten o'clock when we started the frantic drive to Bristol (my secretary by now having been able to make the necessary arrangements). It had to be the day, of course, that there was a diversion off the M5 and we arrived with three minutes to spare at Broadcasting House in Whiteladies Road with the usual parking difficulties. After boxing in someone else's car in the hope that they would not want to leave before us we presented ourselves, breathless, at reception to be confronted by the Corporation's most officious commissionaire, or security officer as they have now become.

Even to these hardened gentlemen I suppose that three total strangers claiming to have a telephone call coming through any moment from Saudi Arabia would seem a bit far-fetched. Infuriatingly polite, he seemed to take great delight in telling me that the Head of the Network Production Centre to whom I demanded to speak was in America and the Audio Manager, whom I next requested, was on leave. Meanwhile the ever-present BBC clock was showing it to be several minutes after eleven-thirty and the red second hand was sweeping round relentlessly. It was only when I eventually got through to the Network Editor, Radio, Michael Bowen, that the portcullis was raised and we found ourselves in a studio with John Taylor on the end of a perfect line to Riyadh where he assured us it was, 'very hot indeed. Good haymaking weather, about 130 degrees Fahrenheit.' We recorded the interview successfully but, before going up to the BBC Club for a well-earned drink, I decided to go and have a word with the security man. Instead of the obstructive Scot I found an easy-going fellow West Countryman. The other chap had gone off-duty. Oh well, he was only doing his job, I supposed, and we could have been going to blow the place up.

We got back to Pebble Mill and edited the telephone call in. It worked like a dream; even the footsteps sounded absolutely authentic. On Monday a colleague said: 'Liked your programme on Saturday. Didn't think the chap in Saudi said much, though.' Others, fortunately, were kinder.

I suppose we were cheating in a way, putting the programme together like that and I would not want anyone to think that it happened very often. In any case, we did not have much option, once the original arrangements had failed.

The only other occasion on which the programme was not actually completed at breakfast time was when we visited Henry Heemskerk in Holland. He came at the end of a European marathon trip undertaken by David Richardson and me and we simply could not get there in time for breakfast. So we did it over coffee; and we still had some spoons to rattle.

One instance when we nearly did not have the sound effects our listeners have come to expect was when we recorded a programme with Jack Boddy, then general secretary of the National Union of Agricultural and Allied Workers, in a studio at Broadcasting House in London. The restaurant staff kindly provided a Continental breakfast of crisp rolls, butter, marmalade and coffee—with paper plates and plastic cups and spoons. You cannot have a good rattle with a plastic spoon and no saucer so urgent phone calls had to be made to break the usual rules which forbid the removal of proper crockery from the restaurant. We got our cups, saucers and spoons, and Jack was able to talk to us against the background of the occasional tinkle.

I shall never forget the studio manager in Brussels once where we were doing one of our first Continental breakfasts, with Tom Cowen whom the NFU had recently sent out to look after its interests in the EEC. We had borrowed a studio from Radio Television Belge and their chap was keen to show us that the BBC was not the only organisation in the world capable of high standards. He bustled around moving microphones and acoustic screens trying to achieve the ultimate in perfection when suddenly, to his utter amazement, trays of breakfast were carried in; croissants crunched and teaspoons tinkled ruining, in his view, all the elaborate preparations he had made. He threw up his hands in horror and retired to the cubicle and sulked: but still produced an excellent result.

Although the monthly breakfast conversations are to most of *On Your Farm*'s listeners the most popular item, we do get

PLATE 1. Post-programme relief: taken after the 100th breakfast edition of *On Your Farm* in 1981.

PLATES 2 AND 3. *Left*, the 7th Earl Stanhope, soldier, politician, landowner and farmer.

Below, Chevening House, where I was a frequent guest during the war, photographed before the controversial alterations which took place following the death of the owner.

PLATE 4. A Tatler-esque but not very typical picture of my parents during the fifties: my father was one of the first to be knighted by the Queen after her accession.

PLATES 5, 6 AND 7. *Above left*, the 'junior sub-editor', complete with moustache and pipe, at work in 1949 at Sun Printers in Watford where *Farmers Weekly* used to go to press.

Above right, A. G. Street, author of *Farmer's Glory* and many other books, whose regular *Farmers Weekly* article I was given to sub on my first day as a journalist.

Below, near Lille in 1958 with John Keeling of Elsoms (left) and M. André Blondeau, breeder of Bersée, one of the most successful French wheats ever to have been imported.

PLATES 8 AND 9. *Above*, planning a studio discussion in the more leisurely days of the early sixties with (left to right) Warwickshire farmer George Steele, the late Sandy Macdonald of the Milk Marketing Board and Professor Eric Lamming of Nottingham University.

Below, an outside broadcast from the Shropshire and West Midlands Show, again during the early sixties, with my secretary Jane Dick, Don Park, then principal of Shropshire Farm Institute, and Peter Buckler (holding microphone). The moustache has gone; the pipe followed soon afterwards.

PLATES 10 AND 11. *Above*, getting mud on the boots of *The Archers* scriptwriters—a visit to Roly Morris's farm in Worcestershire in 1972 with (left to right) Brian Hayles, young Andrew Morris, Mr. Morris, Norman Painting (who wrote as Bruno Milna and also, of course, plays Phil Archer) and script editor Malcolm Lynch.

Below, a typical *Archers* script conference at Pebble Mill at which the next month's story lines are thrashed out. Going clockwise from the Agricultural Story Editor's back in foreground we have Helen Leadbeater (writer), Diane Culverhouse (programme assistant), William Smethurst (Editor) and writers Margaret Phelan, James Robson and John Fletcher.

PLATES 12 AND 13. *Above*, just to prove that the *On Your Farm* breakfast conversations do actually take place over the breakfast table. Getting ready to go at the North Berwick home of Lord Stodart, then Anthony Stodart, Secretary of State, Ministry of Agriculture. Also in the picture are Dick Silver adjusting his mike, secretary Jane Weir, Lady Stodart and David Richardson.

Below, Michael Clark, in the *On Your Farm* studio at Pebble Mill, translating his handwriting for the benefit of production secretary Ann Stephens.

PLATES 14 AND 15. *Above*, one of agriculture's most successful broadcasters—Nancibel Gregory who farmed until her death in 1977 near Chipping Norton in Oxfordshire. A regular and much-appreciated contributor to *On Your Farm*.

Left, the legendary Tom Parker of Hampshire—still riding in his eighties. Our breakfast programme with 'The Guv'nor' was the most popular in the series and was twice repeated by public demand.

complaints. One of the most persistent niggles is that we do not give women a fair hearing. We all know that behind every successful man there's supposed to be an astonished mother-in-law but, according to our listeners, behind every successful farmer there is a hard-working farmer's wife. I certainly would not disagree but challenge you to get them to talk. Believe me I have had enough letters now accusing me of being a male chauvinist pig to make it number-one priority. In fact I have regarded it as important right from the start. Mrs Smith played a vital part in the very first breakfast we did and I have tried to encourage the women folk in every subsequent one, but quite often they just do not want to say anything. Some even absent themselves from the room having served the breakfast, and one went so far as to push it through the hatch without coming in at all. Some just make it clear the night before that they do not want to be involved; others promise that they will take part and change their minds—sometimes after the first question has been put. It cannot be because they do not like us because we always seem to get on very well before and after the recording. It cannot be because we do not know how to interview women—some of our very best programmes have been with members of the fair sex. Think of the one with Mary Macrae and her wonderful mother Lady Phyllis near Bury St Edmunds; or the visit to that fantastic character Nancibel Gregory on the Cotswolds; or when we breakfasted with the left-wing NUAAW-sponsored MP, Joan Maynard. Then there was our conversation with Ann Wheatley-Hubbard in Wiltshire (no one complained that they did not hear enough of Mr Wheatley-Hubbard); and one of the most successful of all our programmes was with the Vice-Chairman of the Small-farmers' Association, Pippa Woods, on her farm in Devon.

Yet I have to admit that too often the lady of the house makes only a token appearance. I think there are several reasons for this. We have usually selected our 'host' because of his personality and achievements. The undeniable fact of life is, however unacceptable to our feminist listeners, that most farmers, landowners, farmworkers, chairmen of marketing boards, directors of agricultural companies and Ministers of Agriculture are men. I said earlier that one of the criteria for choosing people for this particular programme is that they actually want to do it. I think I have demonstrated that it is hairy enough at times doing these programmes with willing participants, let alone unwilling ones. To be willing manifests an element of outgoingness which may not be present in the spouse, however important her role in the business. We have had unwilling partakers burst into tears in the middle of a programme which does not really help anyone. We have often joked that for my last *On Your Farm* they would come to breakfast with me and subject me to some of the tortures to which I am supposed to have exposed other people for twenty-odd years. My wife, who has been a wonderful support to me in everything I have done, has already made it clear to me that she would not wish to take part.

Another reason why the women are often reticent is that in an old-fashioned way (and farming is still old-fashioned in many ways which is what makes it so agreeable) she regards the farm as being her husband's preserve and any programme centring round it his concern. We try to dispel this but not always very successfully. Sometimes the farmer does not help; he is afraid his wife might blurt out the awful truth about something and so suggests that she keeps a low profile. During the conversation the afternoon before recording one of these programmes we were talking in a light-hearted way to several members of the family when I asked the farmer's wife what sort of things made her husband angry.

'When he can't find his teeth,' she replied amid hoots of laughter. Her husband was not one of those who hooted loudest. In spite of my protestations to the contrary he obviously thought that the same question might come up the following morning across the breakfast table because later on I heard him rehearsing his wife in readiness.

'When they talk to you tomorrow,' he told her insistently, 'tell them how wonderful it is to have the family round you and to see your son and daughter-in-law and grandchildren every day.' He obviously did a very good job because during the recording it was all that we could get out of her.

'Do you come from this part of the country?'

'No,' came the answer, 'but I must say how wonderful it is

to have the family round me and to see my son and daughter-in-law and grandchildren every day.'

We tried a different tack: 'How often do you go into town?'

'Not often, but I must say how wonderful it is to have the family round me and to see my son and daughter-in-law and grandchildren every day.'

She was capable of much more.

The other criticism most commonly voiced about the *On Your Farm* breakfasts is that we favour the bigger farms. It is certainly true that we have been to some very large ones. Twenty thousand acres was the biggest—Frank Arden's place in Lincolnshire. But what a fascinating man. Started with fifty-six acres, trained as a pork butcher, had a secretary who started at 7 a.m. by which time he would have done half the work. But what a pay-off. 'Acres don't interest me,' he said.

Then how about Fred Salmon and his eight thousand acres in the Dukeries; Rex Paterson who when we visited him in 1970 was still farming the best part of nine thousand in Hampshire and Wales; Tom Parker, also in Hampshire, with his four thousand; the Walstons with their block of Cambridgeshire a mile wide and five miles long?

Yes, we've visited some big farmers all right. But what incredible characters all of them have been.

According to Peter Laud's amusing column in the *Birmingham Evening Mail* the programme exists 'to cater exclusively for those farmers fortunate enough not to have to worry about where the money for the next £10,000 tractor is coming from.' He hopes that the *On Your Farm* team will never drop in on his Welsh upland farm but just in case it does proffers a ready-made introduction for the programme: 'Good morning. Today we're waiting for breakfast at Peter Laud's crummy down-at-heel smallholding. Outside there's a fine crop of docks, nettles, thistles and buttercups, and the sheep are in the garden trampling the runner beans.

'We're standing in the kitchen because the dog refuses to let us sit. Peter seems to be screwed up in some pain having fractured his ankle on a pile of building bricks and a baby is offering us some of her soggy toast and smiling at us.

'Mrs Laud is in the yard refereeing a fight between a gander and a cockerel and the postman's van appears to have collided with the front gate.'

Very funny, Mr Laud, but we have also been to see plenty of smaller farmers, you know, some on farms even smaller than your own holding. The Land Settlement Association tenant in Bedfordshire with four or five acres for example; the county council smallholder in Derbyshire with fifty-two; the Hendersons (of *Farming Ladder* fame) in Oxfordshire with eighty-five and plenty with a hundred or two hundred. And even more with no land at all like the farm workers with whom we have shared bacon and egg (their wives had plenty to say!).

Now, as we move well into our second century of breakfast hosts there is one thing which they all have in common—large and small, rich and poor, employer or employee, tycoons, whizz kids and politicians. They are all firm friends of mine, including the ones who were total strangers when I first went a-knocking on the door. Which perhaps exposes both the strength and the weakness of this particular format. We have obviously, from listeners' reaction over nearly fifteen years, been able to produce some absorbing programmes without offending our hosts. But at the same time I wonder whether, as guests, we have given some of them too easy a ride. It is difficult to penetrate too hard when you have got your knees tucked under someone's breakfast table.

FIVE

Making Programmes

It may sound a pretentious thing to say but every programme is a little work of art, the result of creative thought, and would not have existed without the producer—even an offering as modest as *On Your Farm.* The link between a producer and his programme is fundamental; there is no set of rules about making programmes and no producer can effectively work to someone else's instructions. The BBC recognises this by going to enormous trouble to try and appoint the most suitable person—and then leaving him or her to get on with it. There are plenty of people from whom to seek advice if he needs it, ample facilities at his disposal and, within budgetary limits, the world is his oyster. Inside the Corporation the producer rules—unless he makes a pig's ear of it when he is either rapped over the knuckles or, if he does it too often, removed. But until then he is in complete control and it would not be exaggerating the situation to say that no one, not even the Director General, can tell me what to put in *On Your Farm* next Saturday.

All of which places a tremendous responsibility on a producer in his efforts to select and juxtapose a collection of sounds and ideas and fashion them into a fair, constructive and harmonious programme. In trying to do this I, as producer of *On Your Farm*, have not only to please my boss at Pebble Mill and the Controller of Radio 4 and the Managing Director, Radio and the Director General but all those thousands of folk who switch on at quarter past seven on a Saturday morning and who, as I have demonstrated in an earlier chapter, are quick to complain if they do not like what they hear. The discipline of having all one's work displayed to the public ear is considerable. The manager of a bank can make an awful mistake and the odds are that only his regional general manager will know anything about it. An error of fact or judgment in one of my productions is laid open for inspection by anyone who cares to switch on the radio. In agricultural terms it is like farming every field on both sides of the A1; if the drill has a blocked coulter it is impossible to hide the result. No farmer likes bad workmanship exposed to the public gaze and no producer wants a flawed programme to carry his name.

Those of us who produce farming programmes on radio also face additional pressures in that most of us play an active part in the presentation and interviewing. It is unusual in the BBC for a producer both to produce and present a programme. In our agricultural output it is normal practice and has been for a quarter of a century. In introducing my first edition of *A Living From the Land* a few days after joining the Corporation in 1960 I was only following in my predecessor's footsteps. The producers of our early morning *Farming Today* take it in turns to present their own productions; my colleagues who produce *Farming Week* also present the programme, and Ken Ford combines both jobs skilfully in *Gardeners' Question Time*. It seems to have worked well over a long period but it can add considerably to the stress on the producer. Not that I monopolise the presentation of *On Your Farm*. Half a dozen people have had a go over the last twelve months.

The choice of a presenter is a crucial one in the success of a programme. A good one can make a weak item acceptable by what he says before and after it; a poor presenter can kill a strong item stone dead. In the earlier days of agricultural broadcasting it used to be thought that farmers made the best presenters. This was at a time when the advisory and educational aspects of the programmes were paramount and it was felt that farmers would listen to another farmer better than some smart-Aleck of a journalist or professional broadcaster. But times, as I was explaining in Chapter One, have changed. Agriculture has now become one of the most highly sensitive political areas and subject to close scrutiny by pressure groups of all sorts. A measure of the change in its status is there in the roll of Ministers of Agriculture. What was at one time thought to be the graveyard of politicians has proved to be the launching pad for some of today's leaders—Mr Prior, Mr Silkin and

Mr Walker to name but three. Agriculture has become one of the big economic departments of government and the Minister now finds himself halfway up the Cabinet pecking order instead of near the bottom. My feeling, and it is one not shared by all my colleagues, is that it is no longer acceptable for a programme such as *On Your Farm* to have a farmer as its regular presenter. It would be acceptable once a month, perhaps, in a non-controversial edition; but I think it places a farmer in an impossible position when he is asked to present a programme including pieces on contentious subjects like wages or prices, and the producer in an equally impossible position in trying to defend the situation.

This is one of the reasons why listeners to *On Your Farm* hear less these days of one of the most popular figures in farm broadcasting, Michael Clark. Since he started presenting *On Your Farm* fifteen years ago Mike has endeared himself to countless thousands with his warm, patently honest, down-to-earth manner and his mellifluous West Country voice. Unflappable (to a fault, sometimes), liked by everyone, Mike has served the programme well; long may he continue his association with it. We now share him with Harlech Television's farming programme and, of course, his 170-acre dairy farm which used to be in Somerset and now, much to his annoyance, lies in Avon.

'How do you decide what to put in a programme?' is a question I have often been asked and always find difficult to answer. It comes down in the end, I think, to a very long connection with and obsessive interest in agriculture and everything to do with it—coupled with instinct. People expect a cut-and-dried answer which just does not exist. No two programmes are the same—or ever will be with a subject like farming. If the format were similar the content would certainly be different.

It is the same with the other frequently asked question—'How long ahead do you plan your programmes?' I feel that they would love me to say three weeks or three months rather than 'it depends'. Some programmes such as the Royal Show are earmarked, rather than planned, six months ahead while others have still not taken shape on Friday morning as I motor to the studios at Pebble Mill. Time spent planning, although often vital, can have surprisingly little effect on the chemistry of the final mix. Some programmes which have started off on a Friday, when we record, full of promise end up disappointingly while others still with question marks hanging over them at ten o'clock in the morning have turned out to be real crackers by half past six. As I said earlier on we *are* still, fortunately, dealing with human beings.

The most important consideration about any programme is that people are going to want to listen to it because unless they do the whole complex operation amounts to a waste of time. It does not matter how long it took to make, how clever it is, how hard everyone worked; if people switch off (or in the case of a long-running series like *On Your Farm* do not think it worth switching on) it has all been in vain. It is fairly easy, sadly, to satisfy an audience with a light-hearted and superficial programme. It is also very tempting to produce weighty, worthy programmes which are satisfying to make but would bore the pants off most people. The challenge comes in treading that narrow path between the two; in letting a programme say something worth while to as large an audience as possible.

The pattern of the programme varies from week to week. In most months we would tend to have one breakfast edition, one which dealt with a single subject – perhaps conservation or milk marketing or a visit to a specific area or institution – and one or two magazine programmes containing a variety of pieces. I say one or two because superimposed on this pattern is the agricultural calendar with events like the Royal Show and Smithfield, the Oxford Farming Conference and other happenings which we have tended to cover in the past. Then there are our two 'hook-up' programmes, one in the spring and one at harvest, and the various 'Radio 4 on Tour' weeks which from time to time direct our attention in specific directions. We also do the occasional 'Taking the Pulse' edition where we visit a county or a smaller area such as the Yorkshire Dales and talk to interesting people. And in recent years, due to demands on my time from other programmes, I have been in the habit of inviting a colleague to produce one programme each month and whoever is doing it, of course, has the freedom to deal with it as he wishes.

What I am looking for when putting together magazine programmes are variety and balance. Variety of subject, of length of item, of pace, accent, treatment; these are all things I would like to have, although do not always achieve, in a single programme. Balance is something at the back of one's mind all the time—balance between arable and livestock, north and south, hill and lowland, political and practical, employer and employee, landlord and tenant, producer and consumer, so that nobody feels left out for too long.

There is certainly no shortage of sources of material. Every post brings handouts galore. I collected a week's offering one August just to see what it came to. They were sent by about forty organisations and commercial firms and totalled nearly two hundred sheets. And that was in the middle of the 'silly season' when nothing is supposed to happen. There are more than four hundred members of the Guild of Agricultural Journalists who, presumably, all received the same material. I wonder how many trees have to be felled each year to keep us informed.

The Ministry of Agriculture took the prize for sending most handouts with information ranging from Ministerial appointments to sales of potato crisps, from weekly slaughtering statistics to placings of day-old chicks. The National Farmers' Union ran it a close second on a variety of subjects from ragwort through killer dogs to wayleave payments. The remainder came from nearly forty national institutions, marketing organisations, research centres and commercial firms and brought news of, among other topics, Scottish land prices, danger of loose smut, lower mortgage rates and plans to bake a 12½ ton apple pie.

But these handouts are only part of the elaborate arrangements made to inform me so that I can inform our audience. I am also invited to meetings, press conferences and demonstrations galore, to the opening of this, the celebration of that and the award of the other—at each of which I shall be given a press pack in a plastic envelope or encouraged to take copious notes. One learns to be very selective.

Then there are all the farming journals and daily press. We feed upon each other quite blatantly and, I hope, constructively. *Big Farm Weekly* and *Farming News*, for example, go to press on Tuesday. We are in the market until Friday night. They may carry a story which has developed considerably by the time we see the paper on Friday and we may be able usefully to take it a stage further. On the other hand there have been numerous occasions on which something has been said in *On Your Farm* on a Saturday which has been seized on and followed up by one of the farming papers the following week.

Some ideas for programmes come from listeners but the most fertile source is undoubtedly personal contact—with farmers and non-farmers at markets and meetings, demonstrations and dinner parties. The whole thing is like a gigantic snowball with ideas being accumulated for use or rejection all the time.

Programmes involve people and I have found them remarkably co-operative when approached. The initial contact is usually made by telephone and then the tricky bit starts. I am trying to find out over the telephone whether he is the right man for the interview or discussion I have in mind. Meanwhile he is wondering why this nosy fellow from the BBC is asking him a lot of fairly personal questions. At some point – all too soon, from my point of view – I am going to have to ask him if he could take part in a programme or thank him politely for his help and ring off. It could be a simple interview on, say, the use of surplus farm buildings for light industry. The government has asked local authorities to be more liberal in granting planning application and we want to see how it might work out in practice. Enquiries have led me to a farmer whom I have never met and here I am asking the size of his farm, what enterprises he has, how long he has farmed there, whether he has a lot of farm buildings and his views on rural depopulation. All the time I am trying to assess whether he has the right background, is well enough informed, could hold his own in a discussion and would fit in well with the other two speakers whom I have already booked. A lot hangs on this conversation—the whole success of that part of the programme in fact.

The interesting thing is that nine out of ten of the people I invite to take part do agree, sometimes qualifying their acceptance with 'if you think I'm the right chap,' which puts the ball very firmly in my court.

Of course, one cannot always be right and that is why some discussions or interviews never seem to get off the ground. There is a marked divergence here between journalism and broadcasting. When I crossed the great divide my newspaper colleagues used to pull my leg and say how easy life must now be—'all you have to do is stick a mike under someone's nose.' In fact the job is infinitely harder. As a journalist I could take a note from someone without necessarily having to quote it; I could commission an article and if it did not come up to expectations (quite possibly because I had misjudged the writer's ability) I could spike it and send him a cheque and no harm would be done. If I point a microphone or a camera at him, however, it is somehow a different ball game; I enter into a moral contract with him to make some use of it or explain why I have not. If I invite someone into a studio and find that I have made a mistake in my choice there is only one thing I can do and that is to make the best of it. There is no equivalent of shoving his contribution on the spike and paying him off.

Sometimes, of course, it is just an attack of nerves which might succumb to a drop of whisky. The chap who sounded so assured on the telephone can only mumble in the studio. When he appears marginally more confident after one drink there is a temptation to offer him another but therein lies a danger because, if it does not work and he is not used to it, you may find yourself with a contributor in the early stages of inebriation. There is no way that I know of removing a Scotch from someone who has consumed it.

Apart from the fact that I do not like hurting people's feelings there is a purely practical angle to this. With a long-running programme like *On Your Farm*, dealing with a fairly circumscribed domain, I would not find the job any easier if I went round short-changing my contributors. Gates would soon be closed and receivers put down.

As it is, one finds oneself embarrassingly welcome in most situations and, within five minutes of being on a farm, the recipient of the most intimate information from the size of the bank overdraft to the fact that he does not get on with his wife. I remember one occasion when on driving into a yard I ran over a Muscovy duck. I knocked on the door of the house of a man I had never met, and who had nothing to gain from my visit, holding a dead duck in one hand and a microphone in the other. He brushed my apology aside. 'Don't worry. We get two or three killed every week like that.'

I can only recall having the door slammed in my face once. We were doing one of our 'Taking the Pulse' editions of the programme where we arrive unannounced, often with the tape recorder going. The door opened and quickly shut with a loud bang. We were then addressed from the bathroom window by a farmer who relaxed only after we had established that we were not from the now defunct Eggs Board from whom he had been expecting a visit. After that, we got on fine.

Frank Taylor, the Nottinghamshire farmer who used to work on BBC radio and television farm programmes, liked to tell the story of arriving at a location with a film crew who stayed discreetly in the yard while he went to make contact.

'Ah, you're from the fertiliser people,' said the farmer.

'British Broadcasting Corporation,' Frank corrected him.

'Oh, you spread it as well,' replied the incredulous farmer.

During my days on *The Farmers Weekly* I remember arriving once outside a farm where I knew we were going to face a rough reception. We were just deciding how best to approach the farmer when Gordon Cradock, our photographer, leaned forward to reach something and inadvertently sounded a five-second blast on the horn. Not the best way to start a difficult interview.

I was saying earlier that there is no set of rules for making programmes but most producers have established their own personal principles. I certainly have and often get teased by regular contributors who do not always feel as strongly about them as I do. For example, I abhor the use of the word 'problem'—only because it has become grossly over-used and is normally either superfluous or an excuse for laziness. Switch on almost any programme these days and it will not be long before it crops up, often tagged on quite unnecessarily to some noun or other. The garden problem, the breakfast problem, the slimming problem, the travelling problem, the problem of this, the problem of that, the solution to the problem and so on. It is a useful, useless word to tag on when you cannot be bothered to think of the proper one. It was introduced by sloppy interviewers and has now, as often happens, been adopted by interviewees and is self-proliferating. It is almost certain that if it is used in a question it will be returned in the answer; interviewees seem unable to resist repetition. (I had an amusing example of this not long ago when I was interviewing a forestry enthusiast about tree planting on his estate. He was justifying a particular piece of afforestation by the fact that the land was too steep for anything else. I pointed out: 'It's not too sheep for a steep to climb,' and before I could correct myself he came back: 'No, it's not too sheep for a steep, I grant you.')

A much-used radio interviewer used to boast that it was possible to accomplish any interview with just four questions. The first was 'What is the problem?' The interviewee was so accustomed to the fact that life is assumed to be full of problems that an answer was always forthcoming. The second question was 'What are you doing about it?' The third, the catch question, was 'Why didn't you do this earlier?' and the last, guaranteed to be good for an answer: 'What of the future?'

I was much amused to hear one of our leading interviewers come unstuck on a phone-in programme:

'And now we have Mr Bloggs on the line from Hemel Hempstead,' he said. 'What's your problem, Mr Bloggs?'

'Come again?' from Hemel Hempstead.

'I said "what's your problem?" Mr Bloggs.'

'I haven't got a problem.'

The interviewer starts to show signs of impatience. 'Well, what's worrying you, then?'

To which Mr Bloggs replied: 'Nothing's worrying me. I just wanted to say . . .'

No one has any 'problems' in *On Your Farm* if they want to stay with the programme and it is amazing how infrequently it crops up. It does not really come into the category of vogue words which come and go. 'Situation' gave us a bit of trouble a few years back – again normally used quite superfluously – and I wrote a piece about the two words for our house magazine but got stuck on the title. Should it be 'The Problem Situation' or 'The Situation Problem'?

Another word we use very sparingly in *On Your Farm* is 'could', where it becomes the most important verb in the sentence. You know the sort of thing. 'Today we're going to hear about a development which *could* lead to the setting up of a meat marketing board in this country'—not 'is likely to' or 'will', or even 'stands a very strong chance of'. In most cases you might safely add in parentheses 'but is extremely unlikely to'. Its use often simply means either 'I haven't done enough research to find out whether a more specific verb might be applied' or 'We're short of an item and this one might just get by if you don't take too much notice of the qualification implicit in the verb.' In most cases where it is appropriate the item would best be kept until something more useful might be said about it.

I deplore the use of the term 'lady' where the more homely 'woman' is more fitting, as indeed it usually is. I would not lean too heavily on Partridge who says on the subject in his *Usage and Abusage—a guide to good English*:

> lady, which has a social – almost a Society – connotation, should not be used as a synonym for 'woman', any more than 'gentleman' should be used as a synonym for 'man'. Only those men who are not gentlemen speak of their women friends as 'lady friends', and only those women who are not ladies speak of themselves as 'charladies' and their men friends as 'gentlemen friends'.

In this egalitarian age Partridge's distinction may not be universally acceptable (although it appears in the latest editions). No, I simply object to the way in which 'lady' is ousting the perfectly honourable term 'woman'. I actually heard someone refer in a phone-in programme to a 'lady terrorist'. So we stick to women farmers in *On Your Farm*.

We try to avoid the use of 'factoids', the useful term coined for manufactured facts which become 'facts' only through their constant repetition by the media. It is a well known factoid that Peter Walker made a million by the time he was thirty. He denied it in *On Your Farm* but that does not prevent its being repeated. If we quote a factoid, and it is sometimes necessary to, we endeavour to make it clear that it is a factoid and not an established fact.

I have a personal phobia regarding the indiscriminate use of singular nouns with plural verbs and vice versa. To me the government, the council, the committee, the union are singular—so the Government has asked, the council is embarking, the committee does not know and the union was unanimous. Others regard them as plural which is fair enough. But frequently we hear in the same programme that the Israeli government *have* but the Danish government *has*. There is not much I can do about it except to try and make sure that the Home Grown Cereals Authority and the British Wool Marketing Board march in step in *On Your Farm*.

It must be obvious by now that you cannot produce programmes for twenty-odd years without developing likes and dislikes. I find I have no wish to join the 'that report by' school of presenters. I know not how many seconds a day they save by leaving out the verb but it jars every time I hear it. I also, as I mentioned earlier, dislike the over-use of Christian names over the air. It seems to me that to Tom, Dick and Harry everyone has the opposite effect to that intended; rather than embracing the listener I feel that it tends to exclude him, leaving him somehow outside the cosy little chat which appears to be going on between old friends in the studio. Obviously it cannot always be avoided; it is hard to call someone you have known well for half a lifetime 'Mister' but I certainly do not rush to call Mr Bloggs, whom I have only just met, Joe. I think it is particularly important in programmes dealing with farming where a strong element of old-fashioned formality survives.

Lastly, concerning the people who take part in the programme, I try to avoid the phoneys, the dilettantes, the theorists, the purveyors of second-hand opinion where possible (and it is not always possible). I am a great believer in talking to people who have actually done it rather than think it could be done; those who have made money rather than feel it could be made.

At the risk of appearing pompous I feel sure that the 'house style' we have developed for *On Your Farm*, which incorporates these principles, has contributed greatly to its success and helped to keep it on the air for so many years.

No programme is perfect—or no run-of-the-mill programme like *On Your Farm* is perfect. It could always do with more time, more effort spent on it. But in my experience there comes a point where you have, so to speak, to draw a line under it and say 'That's as good as I can make it bearing in mind that I've got another one to do next week and the week after, that I have *The Archers* and other editorial responsibilities to discharge—and that I have a wife and four children.'

If I am invited to speak about *On Your Farm* I usually suggest when asked for a title 'Why last Saturday's programme wasn't as good as it should have been.' I know that this will always give plenty of scope, whatever the date of the meeting. I sometimes say, jokingly, that I would like a minute or so at the end of every edition to explain the glaring imperfections. As it is no one knows about the contributor who fell ill at the last minute, the line from Aberystwyth which failed to materialise, the tape recorder which played up or the piece which got delayed in the post.

However, I suspect that the day you could guarantee the success of a programme would be the day I would begin to lose interest.

SIX

Both Sides of the Camera

For the first twelve years of producing a weeky radio programme, until I got caught up in *The Archers*, I was heavily involved in television—as a reporter, interviewer, director and, for a brief period, as a producer. Most of the work was done for the regional magazine programme *Midlands Today* and its predecessors but I contributed also, during the early sixties, to the Sunday *Farming* programme and produced it for about six months in 1964 when the regular producer was otherwise engaged.

I got off to a bad start. I had been invited as the BBC's Midland Region agriculture correspondent to take part in a review of the year. I had done a piece partly to camera and partly over film and was then supposed to cue my successor. It was a live programme from the cramped studio at the old Broad Street premises in Birmingham and such was the camera set-up that I had to turn the wrong way to introduce him, in other words left when he was sitting on my right. So, looking at nobody at all, I found myself saying 'And now for a review of the industrial scene here is my colleague . . .' Without being able to see him I could not remember his name; I swung round to glimpse his comfortable figure on my right and then turned left again and finished off '. . . Jeffrey Preece.' I left the studio as soon as we went into film, convinced – wrongly, as it turned out – that my television career was over. No one seemed to have noticed. That early setback taught me a lot and helped me to cope with some of the fun and games which were to follow.

The first time I did an interview for the Sunday television programme *Farming* I had my leg well and truly pulled. We were in a particularly mucky yard on a farm in Leicestershire with a lot of slurry about and the film crew kidded me into allowing them to thread the microphone cable up inside my trouser leg. When I questioned the need I was assured that it was standard practice and that if I wanted to make the grade in television I had better grin and bear it. 'Do you mean that Alan Whicker has to put up with this?' I asked, as the dirty cable rubbed against my thigh. 'Constantly,' they affirmed; 'and worse!' It does not really pay to argue with a film crew. They have all sorts of ways of getting their own back. So they had their joke and later allowed me to buy them a round of drinks.

The sort of thing I was doing for the regional magazine was totally different from my radio work. I was popularising or attempting to explain agriculture to a general audience and striving all the time to relate modern practices and policies to the price and quality of the end-product—food. The people who were watching were the ones who were footing the bill – either as taxpayers or consumers – and were assumed to be interested in what was happening to their money. I took all sorts of props into the studio, crops of every description from sprouts and carrots to sugar beet and sheaves of corn; food of various kinds—joints of meat, loaves of bread, anything we needed to make a point. It became a standing joke. 'What is it this time?' I would be asked as I staggered past the commissionaire with a bushel box. Livestock was included—chickens, turkeys, piglets, lambs; we drew the line at anything bigger. After all we had to go up two flights of stairs to the studio.

One day Dan Slater was persuaded to bring a litter of young pigs on one of the many occasions over the last thirty years when pig farmers were threatened with ruin. Dan farmed on the borders of Worcestershire and Herefordshire and was, in the early sixties, Midland farming's angry young man. He was an interviewer's dream, prepared always to blurt out the awful truth without any regard for his own or anyone else's interest. I remember interviewing him once round one of his apple trees when he was trying to explain to the viewing public that although he was making a fortune at that time out of selling unripe fruit it was not worth buying. Most farmers would have pocketed the money and kept quiet, thinking what fools the public were but it made Dan furious to think that his unripe, scarcely edible apples were making twice as much as his top-quality ripe fruit would be in a fortnight's time.

He had brought apples, lettuce and tomatoes into the studio at various times to demonstrate a point but on this particular evening it was piglets. The studio staff was delighted to have something unusual to point a camera at and quickly constructed a makeshift pen. Dan had a premonition and said to me quietly: 'There is absolutely no way I am having one of those things on my knee during the interview.' He knew that in the past he had been asked to hold a basket of tomatoes or a couple of lettuce but he was making it clear that he was drawing the line at pigs; they were for driving not nursing. But television directors can be persuasive people and five minutes later Dan was caressing a silky piglet as he answered my questions.

He went on to become a most effective horticulture correspondent on both radio and television programmes until he gave up farming in the seventies.

The approach, as I say, had to be different from that used for farming programmes, even when one made allowances for the eavesdropping audience, and I was often doing the same story for both my radio programme and the regional television magazine. A piece about a farmer who had invented a mechanical foot-trimmer for sheep in *On Your Farm*, for example, would have concentrated on how the machine worked, the cost, application and effectiveness. For the *Midlands Today* audience my introductory piece had to be much more explanatory:

> One of the chores we all have to put up with from time to time is cutting our finger nails. But I wonder how many people, apart from farmers, realise that sheep need to have their nails cut regularly as well.
>
> Their nails – or hooves I suppose we ought to call them – grow something like an eighth of an inch a month, about the same rate as our finger nails. When you keep them in the hills, with a lot of rock and stony ground, they tend to wear them down naturally (I don't suppose that the Ancient Britons needed to cut *their* nails very often) but when they're kept, as a

> lot of sheep are these days, on lush pastures, unless they have the growth removed regularly they are liable to get a disease called foot rot. I expect you've seen sheep limping about or sometimes feeding on their knees—well, the odds are that they've got foot rot.
>
> Trimming sheep's feet by hand takes a lot of time and it's not always easy to find the labour these days even if a farmer can afford it. A skilled man can deal with about a hundred sheep a day but because it's such a time-consuming job it tends to get put off—and that's where the trouble starts.

Once or twice a week I would find myself, either at my suggestion or the news editor's, off filming somewhere or in the studio or quite often both; much of the filming was done mute and needed to have a commentary dubbed and to be introduced from the studio. Or the film might well be used to set the scene for a studio interview. We were not normally over-blessed with staff; I quite often had to direct the film as well as do the interview, having set it all up, then possibly write a commentary and go into the studio as well. As we were sometimes filming at three o'clock for a six o'clock programme there was not much margin for error. On the other hand it enabled us to deal with some quite serious subjects—often Midland aspects of national issues. In 1970, for instance, the government produced a report on the condition of our soils. On the day on which it was released in London we were able to flesh out the bare announcement of its publication on the national news with what it revealed regarding the Midlands. The script looked something like this:

> *To Camera*
> There's a broad band of heavy land which runs right across the middle of England where the trouble has been occurring. It's coloured dark green on the maps in this report (AP opens report and points) and if I tell you that about two-thirds of the East Midlands and half of the West Midlands is coloured green you'll see how important it is. Some of the worst land is in Warwickshire where I am at the moment—there's 200,000 acres in the country which according to this report is liable to break down under adverse conditions.

Film of Soil
Now the report states that there's nothing wrong with the fertility of this land at all—it's the structure of the soil which is causing concern. The soil's made up of millions of little particles and when it's in a healthy state there are air spaces between them and room for the water to drain away. When a soil gets damaged these particles all get squashed together, the air gets squeezed out, the water can't get away and that's where the trouble starts. You can't get a decent seed bed – the soil won't break down properly – and crops don't grow very well.

To Camera
Well, that's *how* the trouble is caused; now for the reasons *why*. It's all to do with changing farm practices, aided and abetted by a couple of particularly wet years—1968 and 69.

Film of Cattle and Sheep
Over the last ten or fifteen years arable farming has tended to pay better than beef cattle or sheep. So there has been less farmyard manure going on to the land and also less grass which contributes a lot of organic matter. So these heavy soils become more vulnerable to damage because they have less organic matter in them.

Film of Machinery Working
At the same time there has been more and more machinery used on the land and all the tractors and implements are getting bigger and heavier. And because of the need to get the most out of the equipment and because of the wet weather farmers have had to harvest and cultivate when they should have kept off. And so the soil has been damaged and crop yields have fallen.

To Camera
If you have heavy land in your garden you'll know how easy it is to mess up and how you have to avoid working on it when it's wet. A farmer can't always afford to be so patient. Fortunately, though, it seems that no damage has been done which can't be undone and the report goes on to make several strong recommendations.

The rest of the item dealt briefly with the report's conclusions as they affected the Midlands. The whole piece lasted only about two and a half minutes but the effort involved was considerable. First I had to read a very thick report and try and distil the guts of it, as it affected our region, into a few hundred words. Then I had to find a suitable location—land of the type referred to, in the area referred to, with a friendly farmer (who was not going to get anything out of it) with heavy machinery working and somewhere to film sheep and cattle. As I was not sure which bits were going, in the end, to be the pieces to camera (you are never sure how the film will turn out and library film, though useful on occasions, can be disastrous), I had virtually to learn the piece by heart (I started in television too soon for automatic prompting devices and there was usually no one to hold up idiot boards). But there was a lot of satisfaction when a piece like that went well. Alas it did not always go well.

There was the time we filmed the cider apple story, for instance. Bulmer's, the Herefordshire firm of cider makers, had been doing a lot of research into mechanising the gathering of the fruit. The time-honoured method, still largely practised in the area, is to pick up the fruit by hand into buckets which are then tipped into sacks. But the firm which at that time was using 50,000 tons of apples a year had tried out several other systems including one in which a tractor-mounted shaker seized the tree trunk and vibrated it, causing the apples to fall on to a big nylon sheet which was then wound in, tipping the apples on to an elevator and thence on to a lorry. The idea of our short film was to show the various methods of collecting the fruit. We were to start with a bunch of women grubbing under the trees and follow this by a machine which worked on the vacuum-cleaner principle, sucking the apples up off the orchard floor. We would then show the tractor–shaker moving in, gripping the tree, shaking the apples. Finally there was to be film of the apples being loaded up, driven off and tipped at the factory into one of the huge reception pits. The filming went off without a hitch, the firm was very accommodating in providing all the shots we needed and for once we were not faced with the usual panic since it was not scheduled for screening until the following day.

The next morning I was busy with *On Your Farm* so I wrote a commentary to the right length and sent it down to Broad Street. A good film editor can cut a film very effectively to fit a written commentary and about four o'clock that afternoon I had a telephone call from him.

'You'll be very pleased with the film,' he told me. 'I've managed to hit off virtually every line of the script.'

I had worked with him for years and knew I had nothing to worry about. 'Fine,' I said. 'I'll come down about half past five and have a look before we go on.'

When I reached the studio the usual pre-programme pandemonium reigned. Guests were being welcomed, interviews rehearsed, camera angles tried out and Tom Coyne, the presenter, was pacing up and down the corridor learning his lines. No one was very interested in showing me the cider apple film. At about ten to six they ran it through and to my mounting horror it bore no relationship to the script whatsoever. Not a single word fitted.

What, I asked the producer, was I to do? If mine had been the only panic he might have been able to give it more attention but he had two or three others on and it was rapidly approaching transmission time. 'I don't know, mate,' was all he could manage. 'We've only just got time to spool the film back. You'll have to busk it.'

So 'busk' it I did. I struggled through, ad-libbing a commentary as the pictures came up, and it was not until I got out of the studio that I found out what had happened from a very apologetic film editor. He had cut the film and hung all the pieces, several dozen of them, from the rack and then left it to a trainee to join them all together. This he had done, very neatly, but in the reverse order. We did not have the tractors running backwards—unfortunately, since that would have made it unusable. What we did have was a very carefully edited film assembled from start to finish in reverse order. So the first shot was of a load of apples being tipped into the reception pit at the cider factory and the last a group of women on their hands and knees picking the apples up. This, as you might imagine, involved me in some pretty tricky explanation since each stage of the proceedings was being shown before the one it should have followed.

'Well, there are the apples arriving at the factory,' I volunteered, 'being brought from the orchard . . . and there they are being tipped into the lorry . . . off this elevator.' By this time I had realised what the form was and could see trouble ahead—like apples landing on the nylon sheet before they left the tree and before the tractor had backed up to the tree and gripped the trunk with the shaker. 'You're probably wondering how the apples got onto the sheet . . . well they're shaken from the tree . . . and there's the shaker moving in to do its work.' And so on to the last shot.

Fortunately I knew the story very well or I could never have got away with it; even so it was not an experience I would like to repeat. But it had a curious sequel. The following day I rang the public relations man at Bulmer's to apologise. I knew that the chairman of the company had been holding a party the previous evening to view the film and thought I had better get in first with an explanation. I was about to embark on it when the PR man interrupted me: 'Look, before you go on I must say how fantastic we all thought the film was last night. The chairman was thrilled to bits.'

I do not regard it as part of my job to provide thrills for company chairmen, but the firm had been extremely co-operative in providing everything we needed for the filming. They moved people and machinery around to suit us and held the job up at times, so I did feel that I ought to account for the previous evening's debacle. However, it did make me wonder whether we were proceeding in the right direction if we could carefully cut a film in one order, assemble it in the opposite order and delight everyone in the process. Or did they really all feel that this was the BBC being clever again and no one liked to question why the apples fell off the tree before they were shaken? Or were they all already stoned on cider cup? We shall never know.

Many of the pieces I used to do for *Midlands Today* and its predecessors were slants on national events I was covering for my own radio programme *On Your Farm* and *its* predecessor. I would let the news editor know that I was going to, say, the British Veterinary Association Congress or the Oxford Farming Conference and ask him whether he was interested in a piece. I would perhaps point out that one of the subjects for discussion particularly affected the Midlands or that one of the speakers was a regional personality. Then he would probably get me to telephone the following morning to see whether it looked a promising story and, if so, make arrangements for me to do a report or an interview from another studio. One occasion on which I was usually contracted to provide a daily piece was from the annual meeting of the National Farmers' Union, in London. I remember on one occasion being most unpopular with delegates for interviewing a farmer in a dinner jacket. He was going on to the Union's annual dinner and had decided that it was safer to change before coming to the studio, but it was felt that he had created quite the wrong image at a time when farmers were campaigning for more money.

Doing the reports from the NFU AGM involved going to the television studio in the basement of Broadcasting House at Portland Place which at that time left a great deal to be desired by a visiting reporter like me. You found your way into a totally bare studio except for a couple of chairs, a microphone, a green light mounted on a six-foot-high stand and a mechanical camera. No human being sullied the place with his or her presence. The first time I ever had to use it I walked in clutching my notes and suddenly heard a disembodied voice boom out: 'Sit down.' I did. 'No, not there,' the voice boomed out again; 'the other chair.' I sat there with the programme due to start in about five minutes wondering where the comforting floor manager was when without warning the camera started to move towards me. It came, for all the world like a Dalek, to within about two feet of where I was sitting, had a good look at me and decided to retreat. It then tracked in and out two or three times and took up a stance four or five feet away and lapsed into its previous comatose state.

I sat there waiting for something to happen, watching the seconds being swept into non-existence by the red second hand of the studio clock. It was now past the start of the programme; they were unlikely to use my piece very early on but on a thin night for news I could not be certain. I spoke to the invisible presence.

'What time am I on?'

'Don't know. We'll give you a green,' came the reply.

I spent the next ten minutes watching the tiny green light on top of the slender pole, afraid to look at my notes in case I should be buried in them when the light went on, waiting to do a relaxed piece to camera. Eventually the green light shone and I did my one minute thirty seconds, hoping but without any way of knowing, that Tom Coyne had used the cue material I had telephoned from the NFU meeting earlier on. I left the studio a nervous wreck and went upstairs to telephone the *Midlands Today* office.

'That was fine,' they said. 'You looked a bit startled when we came to you.' I told them that they might appear a little unsettled if they had spent the previous ten minutes staring fixedly at a tiny light bulb. Anyway, I went on, there was no way I was doing a report the following night unless I had a monitor set to see what was going on in the *Midlands Today* studio. Which seemed reasonable.

I turned up the following evening, having been assured that the monitor would be there, and it was. Otherwise the situation was unchanged. I sat in the chair I had been in the previous night only to hear: 'The other one, please.' There was no sound from the monitor set but I assumed that they would turn it up once the programme started. They didn't and I embarked on, if anything, an even worse ordeal than the previous evening. Every time Tom Coyne appeared I tried to lip read his links to see if he was cueing my piece. It was hopeless. At one point he appeared with that particularly genial look which I always thought he kept for agricultural inserts and I could have sworn his lips framed the word 'farming' and made sure I was not looking startled. But no; no sooner had he finished speaking than up came a picture of a zebra crossing. After I had psyched myself up twice more needlessly, he eventually introduced my report (I swear without mentioning farmers or farming) and the green light went on. As soon as I had finished my one minute twenty seconds I complained loudly to the void—but to no effect. Feeling that there must be easier ways of earning a living, I went upstairs and once again telephoned *Midlands Today* with another ultimatum.

The following night we had a monitor with sound—but still no sign of human life.

Apart from frequently appearing 'startled' on these occasions I was often ribbed for looking miserable but, as I used to tell people, when most of your reports are about some awful catastrophe – gales, frost, floods, drought or fowl pest or foot and mouth – you can hardly appear grinning from ear to ear as a market gardener surveys the ruins of his glasshouse or a farmer's precious herd is destroyed. I seemed to spend an awful lot of time interviewing people about ruined crops or threatened livestock.

Some reports are harassing for other reasons. One that was particularly memorable was when I had been to a farming conference in Cheltenham one day to record some interviews for *On Your Farm*, having also offered to do a television report for *Midlands Today*. I had suggested two subjects which were going to be discussed there—one was the rapid increase in size of farm machinery and its implications and the other was continuous cereal growing on the Cotswolds. They opted for the machinery one and, because I had to go on to London after the conference for a meeting that evening, arranged for me to do it from the dreaded London studio. I concentrated first on getting my radio material, knowing that I should have plenty of time on the train journey to sort out the television piece. And so it worked out. By the time I had got to Swindon I had it planned. At Reading I had finished writing and timing it and when we reached Paddington I had learned it more or less by heart. It was about a quarter past five; I would be there nicely for the programme at six.

Walking through Brunel's fine station, familiar to me since boyhood, I became aware of my own name coming through the loudspeakers. Station announcements are meant for other people and I had to listen two or three times to make sure I was not imagining it, but there it was, as clear as station announcements ever are: '. . . Mr Anthony Parkin of the BBC to the Station Master's office.' It sent a shiver through me of the kind one used to get on receiving a telegram or seeing a policeman walking up the drive. With a wife and four children . . . So it was with some relief that I received the message that the *Midlands Today* office wished me to telephone.

'Ah Tony, thanks for ringing. You're doing a piece for us tonight?'

'Yes, just on my way now.' I looked at the clock and saw that the programme was due to start in half an hour.

'Well look, we don't want the piece on machinery—Peter's doing something on industrial machines and it might clash. Could you do the other bit—what was it, something to do with cereals?'

'Hang on,' I began. But it was no use.

'About one forty-five, two minutes at the outside. OK? Must go. See you.' And the telephone clicked off.

I raced outside and found a cab, scrawled a few headings on the back of an envelope as we made our way through the rush hour to Broadcasting House. Down in the familiar austerity of the studio the remote-controlled camera tracked in and out and finally stopped, the green light eventually blinked and I delivered my report on the significance of growing cereals year after year on the same field. The next day someone said to my wife: 'Saw your husband on TV last night. Thought he looked a bit tired.' I wonder whether life is like that all the time for the Martin Bells of this world.

As in radio so with television people are normally extremely keen to get in on the act, fortunately for us; in fact with television you sometimes have to stave them off. I was surprised therefore one day at the Royal Smithfield Show to get a positive refusal from the owner of one of the champion cattle when I asked him if he would take part in the show that evening. It was not as though I was asking him to come to the studio; we had live television cameras at Earls Court.

'You television people think you've only got to crook your little fingers and we'll all come running,' he said; 'but you've picked the wrong one here. I'm not interested.'

It had all started an hour or so earlier when, as I sat in our mobile radio studio outside the exhibition hall sorting out coverage of the show for *On Your Farm*, the telephone rang. It was *Midlands Today* who had just heard that Fyfe Robertson was presenting a programme live from Smithfield and that they could use the cameras afterwards. Could I get hold of the champion Hereford (a regional favourite), his owner and the butcher who bought him at the subsequent auction. I said I would do my best and got off to a bad start with the breeder. However, like most farmers he was pretty quick off the mark where his own interests were concerned and while I was following up the initial invitation with a spot of quiet persuasion he had come to the conclusion that what he was turning down was a three-minute television commercial for his pedigree herd. So, without back-tracking, he told me that he was sure that his herdsman would be glad to oblige, adding that the chap in question knew a bit about the media having been a fashion photographer at one time. The herdsman agreed and I arranged for him to be at a certain spot with the champion at about a quarter to six and, with phrases like 'from filming to farming' running through my head I returned to my radio work.

I went back to see the animal sold and to fix up with the buyer for him to join us at a quarter to six. It was a butcher from the north-east who had bought the beast and he struggled free of the crowd surrounding the auction, which was still proceeding, pursued by a long kite's-tail of journalists from the national and agricultural press. Amid the euphoria of the moment, he too told me what I could do with the programme and disappeared in a swarm of press men. Having several radio pieces to see to and not wishing to waste more time I decided to seek out the under-bidder on the grounds that, while the animal eventually went for £1,300, he had been prepared to pay £1,250 and so could make some useful comments. He was highly diffident about taking part. Surely, he said, we wanted the actual buyer but I tried to convince him that he would do the job much better. He still looked doubtful but agreed to meet me just before six at the agreed spot. So instead of the owner I had the herdsman and instead of the buyer I had the under-bidder. All I needed now was for someone to substitute an Aberdeen Angus for the Hereford bullock.

At a quarter to six I pushed my way through the crowded avenues to the appointed spot where two television cameras and their attendant crew waited. The herdsman was there with the champion bullock but there seemed to be a row going on. The butcher who had bought the beast had changed his mind and, perhaps realising the possible publicity value following his attention from the press, was now demanding to take part.

'But,' I pointed out, 'you said you didn't want anything to do with it so I've arranged for the under-bidder to take part.'

'Well, you've got two cameras. You can have one of us on each of them.'

I tried to explain that television did not work quite like that – one camera per person – but then he played his trump card:

'Right. I've now bought the bullock. If I'm not on you don't have the beast either.'

'Leave it to me for a moment,' I said desperately and set off to meet the under-bidder. He had been so reluctant to take part that he might well be persuaded to back down, but no such luck. He had warmed to the idea and looked totally incredulous when I asked him if he would consider standing down. Had I not only a couple of hours earlier persuaded him how suitable he was for the job? Ah well, two butchers were better than no butcher, I thought, as we proceeded back to the cameras. We arrived in time to see the herdsman leading the bullock back to its stall. He had become thoroughly depressed by all the squabbling which had continued during my brief absence and had made up his mind that he would not take part either. So with about two minutes to go to zero hour, when I should have been taking it quietly, thinking what I was going to say, I stood there with one arm round the buyer and the other round the herdsman exhorting them to do the piece and then we could all go and have a drink. They finally agreed, so we lined up with the bullock in the middle, the herdsman at his head, the under-bidder behind, me in front with a hand mike and the new owner at the tail end. I got a cue to start and was halfway through my introduction when a roar of laughter went up from the huge crowd which always seems to gather when live cameras are about. And then I saw the reason why. Between my feet was flowing a stream of liquid from the direction of the bullock behind. Then, as I moved forward to talk to the herdsman the animal did what cattle in that situation often do—it lifted its tail in the air. The butcher, with commendable presence of mind, clapped his arm over its tail and forced it down until I had finished the interviews, including his own, and we were off the air, when Nature could be allowed to take its course. Thank goodness that all radio and television contributions were not as difficult to set up and execute.

I referred earlier to the dangers inherent in a mild over-dose of alcohol. I once got involved in a situation with a television programme I was producing which almost ended in disaster. It was about the production of hops, a fascinating subject. We had filmed over a whole season and also followed the crop up to the Borough in London where much of the dealing took place. The complete film had been edited and the commentary dubbed on so all that remained was to film the introduction. I had decided to do this outside a pub in order to stress the total inter-dependence between hops and beer. Hops are one of the few crops produced on a farm for which there is literally no alternative use if they do not end up in beer. Phil Chater, at that time the Ministry's Hops Adviser in the West Midlands where well over a third of the crop was grown, had already done a magnificent job with the commentary and met us outside a picturesque pub halfway up Clee Hill in South Shropshire.

That was my first mistake. Clee Hill, like half the hills in the country, is said to be the highest spot between there and the Urals and on that account subject to strong breezes—and the sound recordist had forgotten to bring a windshield for his microphone. My second mistake was in not finding out in advance that Phil was not a great drinker. I wanted the opening shot of the film to be of Phil sitting on the bench outside this old pub with a pint of bitter in his hand. He was to swig half of this, wipe his mouth with the back of his hand and then say: 'It's the hops that make this taste so good' and then proceed with the rest of the introduction. Unfortunately, the first take was no good—too much wind. The glass was refilled and we tried take two. 'Cut,' came the cry. And so on.

Each time I insisted that the glass was refilled and drunk halfway because each time I hoped it would be the final take. Meanwhile our presenter was beginning to show signs of 'stress' and I could see the programme opening up with, 'Itsh the hopsh that make thish tashte sho good,' as Phil slid slowly off the seat. We decided to set the bench and table up in a less picturesque but less windy spot which gave our presenter a chance for a walk round. The next take worked perfectly and gave me just the start to the programme I wanted.

Although I have been closely involved on a regular basis with television for more than half my time at the BBC I must admit that I have never felt as much at home there as with radio. This is less a criticism of television perhaps than a comment on my own personality although I must confess that I do find tedious the general assumption that one is in some way superior to the other.

'Are you a television producer manqué?' was one of the first questions put to me by my boss when I started as a radio producer nearly twenty-four years ago. I think I gave him an answer he had not received before: 'No, if anything I suppose I'm a farmer manqué' which was probably true then, although not today.

But it crops up in many forms. I remember going to interview the principal of an agricultural college for women. We had discussed the concept at some length over the telephone, the fact that it was for our Saturday morning programme and the likely audience. I had taken an engineer as we were also to talk to some of the students. He adjusted the microphone on the table and pronounced himself happy. Just as we were to begin the principal remarked: 'I must say you've been most awfully clever in hiding the cameras. I just wouldn't know they were there.'

Then there was the woman who badgered me for a long time to include a piece about selenium poisoning in *On Your Farm* and when I eventually succumbed wrote and complained that it had not been on television.

The main reason why I have preferred radio to television is that, in the sort of programmes we are dealing with it is far easier to approach something like perfection in radio. I am not talking of the big prestige programmes where staff, time and money are no object but the day-by-day or week-by-week programme like *On Your Farm.* Earlier I was talking of the reasons why radio is a more difficult medium to work in than journalism and why the gulf between the conception and the realisation of an idea is necessarily wider. In television, in the sort of programmes we work in, it is a yawning canyon with so many complex processes and areas between the producer and the final production over most of which he has absolutely no control at all. If the film gets scratched in processing, or there is something wrong with the sound, or the back projection jams, or a camera goes down just before transmission, or the automatic prompt plays up, or one of a dozen other calamities happens, any of which can ruin a programme, there is not much a producer can do about it but swear.

A few years ago I was working in Fiji for a couple of months for the Commonwealth Fund for Technical Co-operation and while I was there decided to do an *On Your Farm* breakfast programme with a dairy farmer whose grandfather came from Essex. Early one morning I drove thirty miles north of Suva through the bush to his farm and there against a background of rustling coconut trees we recorded a half-hour's conversation on a miniature cassette recorder not much bigger than a paperback. I drove back to Suva, put the cassette in an envelope and posted it to Pebble Mill. A colleague kindly dubbed the signature tune on at the beginning and end and cut a minute or so out to bring it to the proper length; the programme was broadcast in *On Your Farm* a fortnight after I had recorded it. It made an engrossing half-hour but what a meal we should have had to make of it if it had been television.

SEVEN

Getting a Start

One day in the autumn of 1948 I received a letter from the editor of *The Farmers Weekly* offering me a job as a 'junior sub-editor' at the generous salary of six guineas a week. I could hardly believe my eyes. A junior sub-editor; not the editor and not quite the chief sub, it was true, but still . . . And six guineas a week. That was nearly two pounds more than I was getting as a farm worker. I wrote back accepting and started in October when the harvest was out of the way.

The offer had not come quite out of the blue. I had written earlier to see if there was any chance of a job and had been up for an interview. On being demobbed from the RAF earlier in the year I had gone back to work on the farm in Kent where I had already seen three harvests. It was when I found that because of the post-war bulge I should have to wait at least another year before I could get a place at university that I decided to see if I could find a job as a journalist. I started at the top by writing to the leading farming journal and was overjoyed to be given a chance.

I suppose I had always wanted to write, ever since at the age of eight I had started a magazine at school called ambitiously *Town Talk*. It retailed at 2*d*. a copy round the playground but, presumably because it carried no advertisements, was not a financial success and it folded after half a dozen issues. But not before it had taught me a lesson. It was 'printed' by my father's secretary, an Australian girl who offered me a free paragraph about a Test Match. I knew as much about cricket then as I do now which is virtually nothing and had no idea what the abstruse references to the 'ashes' were all about. The paragraph, it seems, favoured the Australian viewpoint and was challenged by some of those who had been profligate with their twopences and I suffered the ignominy of having to admit that I, as editor, had carried a front-page story which I could not understand. It taught me two things which I have tried not to forget. The first is never to include something in an article – or a programme – which I cannot apprehend, without making it clear that I am taking it on trust. The other is always to beware of free copy. The first story I sold was to the *Kent Messenger*; it was some little-known history about a threatened monument in our village which made the front page and earned me a postal order for 17*s*. 6*d*. (87½p).

The post of junior sub-editor, while not quite as important as it sounded, perhaps, was enough of a challenge to me. I was chucked right in at the deep end by being tossed A. G. Street's article which had to be cut to 1,500 words. I did a rough calculation and saw that I would have to get rid of about 300 words. Now to me, and I suspect thousands of others, A. G. Street was a god. I had been brought up on his books – *Farmer's Glory*, *Strawberry Roan*, *Gentleman of the Party* – and had read his weekly page in *The Farmers Weekly* with reverence. To be handed his manuscript was like Moses being handed the tables on Mount Sinai—except that he had not been asked to sub the words of the covenant.

I deleted the three hundred words with surprisingly little difficulty and then, warming to the task, went on to suggest changing the order of two of the subjects he was dealing with. Would this be all right, I asked timidly. 'Best give him a ring,' I was told. So, a few moments later I found myself explaining to the great one what I wanted to do with his copy. He listened politely until I had finished and then said gruffly: 'Do what you b------ well like with it.' I dealt with his article for the next couple of years but never felt the need to bother him again; he never complained.

One of my jobs in those early days was subbing the 'Answers to Your Questions'—in fact dealing with the whole section. This meant farming out the questions to the appropriate expert and then when the replies were received editing the question down to a few lines (which fitted the answer) and finally making up the pages. I should, perhaps, explain that in those days 'answers' as they were usually known formed a most important part of the paper occupying three or four pages, about ten per cent of the total editorial matter. Their value had not then been challenged by a combined assault from ADAS (Agricultural Development and Advisory Service), the commercial firms and the various facilities offered by such experts as the sugar beet fieldsman or the Milk Board's consultant. There is advice in plenty at the end of a telephone these days or, if you want to show that you are a jump ahead, by punching up one of the teletext pages. But thirty-odd years ago the advice was much sought after and I had to select the ones of most general interest to be published, all the others, of course, receiving answers by post.

The questions were divided arbitrarily for publication into four groups – feeding, veterinary, legal and miscellaneous – so that subjects which did not fit comfortably into the first three were accommodated in the last. The most interesting ones were the legal questions; farmers would, presumably because the service was free, pour out the most intimate details of their private lives for the benefit of our tame lawyers.

Among the first bunch handed over for my attention was one from an unfortunate smallholder who had broken both legs and was encased in plaster and fairly immobile as a result. His bitch was on heat and he had had her tied to the leg of the kitchen table so that he could keep an eye on her from his chair by the fire. Through the window had jumped a neighbour's dog which had ravished her in front of his very eyes. Had he got a claim against the dog's owner? Our legal advice was, on balance, everything considered, probably 'no'. The trouble was that a simple query like that would be buried in five or six pages of illegible handwriting including a great deal of superfluous information. However, it certainly provided good practice in subbing.

They were exciting days to be starting in agricultural journalism. Tom Williams' famous Act of 1947 had set the scene for post-war farming; food was still in very short supply and the technological revolution was just about to begin. The experience of the past coupled with the anticipation of the future provided an invigorating backcloth to current events and we would see old-fashioned Karswood Poultry Spice and new-fangled hormone weedkillers featured alongside reports of the new International Federation of Agricultural Producers of which so much was expected. Farmers had been working flat out along largely traditional lines during the war and agriculture was now poised for blast-off.

Looking back at *The Farmers Weekly* of that time it is interesting to see how much and yet how little change has taken place since. You could order a Berkshire, Essex, Large Black, Large White or Wessex sow out of the small ads. any week, most of which would now only be available through the Rare Breeds Survival Trust, I suspect; but the National Union of Agricultural Workers in those days was calling for wage parity with other industries which is very much part of its stock-in-trade in the eighties (and also, incidentally, demanding the same extra food rations as miners). Pages of the journal were devoted to the names of members of the County Agricultural Executive Committees which, although the war was over, were still a very powerful force in the land; yet a headline of that time 'Better Grass is the Key' could well have been used aptly at least once every decade since, each time the merits of the crop were rediscovered. The letters pages similarly yielded dated references to the virtue of the 20 cwt. bullock but also included a non-farmer's complaint that whereas he read that acres of lettuce were being ploughed in, he was being charged 6*d*. apiece. John Cherrington was being quoted as saying exactly the same thirty-five years ago as he was in 1982, which is no criticism of that well-known Hampshire farmer.

The editor of *The Farmers Weekly* at that time, and indeed into the sixties after I had left the paper, was Malcolm Messer, a brilliant man of great vision with an amazing gift for adopting a low profile when it suited him. But nothing could mask the outstanding contribution he made to agricultural progress over a period of nearly thirty years as editor of what he built into Britain's most powerful and influential farm journal. He used to claim that he had trained half the agricultural journalists in Fleet Street but it was cynically pointed out that if there were any truth in this it was only because he grossly underpaid them to the point where they decided the time had come to move on. It was nearly two years and after I had been married for nine months or so that I managed to wring another guinea a week out of him but when he yielded he did so with ineffable charm.

Messer was a great defender of his staff; once after I had been on the paper for several years an article of mine upset a firm of plant breeders to the point where they threatened to withdraw their advertising unless something was done to redress the matter. 'Tell them we won't take any of their ads. for six months,' was Messer's answer to that one; then he asked me what it was all about. As so often happens it was a case of the truth hurting.

One of Messer's foibles was that he could not bear to see the word 'snack' on an expenses claim and would buzz for the offender and tell him that he did not expect his staff to slum, an unusual and somewhat dangerous attitude in a profession where they used to joke about starting an expenses sheet with the date and then adding it in. He was a great boss and, although he kept me on the barest minimum of a salary all the time I worked for him, I owe him a lot.

The Farmers Weekly was then part of Hulton Press and was housed in the old *Evening Standard* building in Shoe Lane, just off Fleet Street, along with the rest of the Hulton stable. *Picture Post* was in its heyday when I joined the firm, with Tom Hopkinson as editor. I doubt whether a greater concentration of journalistic and photographic talent has ever been concentrated on one paper; Hopkinson himself, James Cameron, Fyfe Robertson (Father of our NUJ Chapel for a number of years), Kenneth Allsop, Robert Kee, Denzil Bachelor, later Trevor Philpott and, of course, Bert Hardy and Slim Hewitt the photographers, to name but a few. There was Stephen Potter, who came to edit *Leader* magazine and Marcus Morris who started what must surely have been the best children's comics ever produced—*Girl*, *Eagle*, *Robin*, and *Swift*; and Randolph Churchill always seemed to be popping into the building. As a young greenhorn I would cram into the lift with them as it wound its way slowly up to the fourth floor where I got out. Bert the liftman had been a deep-sea diver who could not kick the habit of going up and down; it was rumoured that he drove his lift slowly to avoid getting the bends, but whatever the reason the longer it took in that company the happier I was. They did not know me but I knew them and bathed in their reflected glory. Many of the *Picture Post* team found a niche in television when the magazine folded in 1957.

Edward Hulton ran the place on paternalistic lines with an extra fortnight's pay at Christmas and a parcel of toys for one's children. Each week there was a free copy of the entire output of the press from *Picture Post* to *Robin*. There were some members of the staff who would gladly have forgone these attentions in exchange for less proprietorial intervention in editorial affairs but I never had any cause to complain during my twelve years' association with *The Farmers Weekly*.

What was originally planned as a year on the paper before university grew into two as I had to wait for a place until 1950. Although subs are not supposed to write I had managed to get a number of pieces into the *FW* including several carrying bylines. This was all very unofficial; no one ever sent me and I never claimed any expenses. I simply used to chase round every spare moment I had at weekends and in what was left of the evenings on my motor cycle looking for stories. Some of the material found its way into *The Editor's Diary*, some as the odd filler on a news page and occasionally there was a longer piece with the magic byline.

What I lacked in journalistic experience I made up in enthusiasm and what knowledge I had gained as a farm worker and on day-release classes in agriculture. I was living in the heart of good farming country in Kent which seemed to be bristling with interesting developments. One summer evening I was travelling home on the train when I saw a huge farm fire. Without bothering to work out where I was I jumped off at the next station and ran a mile back to the fire to take some pictures and get a story. I was then faced with walking and hitch-hiking back to East Malling station where I had left my motor bike. I could not wait to get to the office next day to have the film developed; one of my pictures would surely make the leader page. Sadly they were a miserable lot and fit only for the waste-paper basket. I blamed the fact that the firemen would not let me any nearer but I think my camera just was not up to it. Which all comes into the category of casting one's bread on the waters, a philosophy I have tried to imbue my children with, and it certainly worked in this case because while I was at university I earned a very useful addition to my modest grant by acting as a freelance for *The Farmers Weekly*.

It was a period of the great pedigree sales at Reading market when auctioneering firms like Harry Hobson and Co. and John Thornton and Co. made themselves and their clients rich as farmers scrambled onto the pedigree bandwagon in those post-war years. The *FW* went to press on a Wednesday and there was usually a job for me reporting from the cattle market. It meant cutting the last lecture of the morning but equally it meant a guinea or even two guineas if it was a show and sale. I would watch the bidding, talk to as many folk as possible, write my piece and then find a telephone box and start dictating:

> A disappointing trade was experienced on the first day of the English Jersey Cattle Society's spring show and sale on Wednesday. Many females did not reach their reserve price and a number of bulls failed to find buyers.
>
> The general level of prices was well below that of last year. A suggestion that intending buyers were waiting to see how the price review would treat milk was advanced as a reason for what one purchaser described as a 'buyer's paradise'.

There was not a great deal of scope for initiative on these occasions. Speed and accuracy were the important elements and finding a vacant telephone box was the most taxing part of the operation. That is not to say that these reports were not taken seriously. They were, and woe betide any reporter who made a mistake in the long list of prices which formed an essential part of them. When you dictated 'T. F. L. Talbott's Leoville Queen 3rd (1948) sold to Mrs and Miss Courtney for 250 guineas' it had to be right.

Reading also, fortunately for me, formed part of what we irreverently referred to as the 'inner circle' of places for holding Ministry conferences for farmers. Maidstone, Reading and Chelmsford were the main stations on the inner circle with the occasional stop in between at Guildford or St Alban's; the outer circle included places like Winchester, Gloucester and Northampton. A lot of these affairs were held in the evenings, often Fridays—not popular with *FW* journalists but very welcome to an impecunious undergraduate. So I got quite a few of these to report and I was not above getting a paragraph or two out of the weekly meetings of the university Agricultural Club which usually attracted strong speakers. As I was reporting them I felt it unethical to ask the questions which were likely to give me a quote so I used to plant them among friends. 'Ask him whether he still thinks British farming's at half cock' I remember saying on the occasion of a visit from Professor 'Mac' Cooper who had made headlines a couple of years earlier by his criticism of our agriculture. Whatever the answer it would almost certainly be quotable, I thought. But I was wrong; he did not want to return to the subject on that occasion and side-stepped the question.

I used to return to the *FW* for a spell during vacations and on one occasion had the embarrassment of being sent to cover a poultry conference being held at my own university which involved lunch in the Senior Common Room where no undergraduate was supposed ever to set foot. My presence was referred to no less an authority than the Vice Chancellor who graciously allowed me to finish my pudding. But even worse was in store. The delegates to the conference, myself included, were to stay the night at my own Hall. Food was still rationed and we used to complain to the Warden that his staff was keeping us short of food, especially bacon, in order to serve it to conferences such as this one during the vacations. So the Warden was not too pleased to welcome me to a sumptuous dinner and generous breakfast with two rashers the following morning. As I was leaving he called me over and said in his rich Scots accent: 'Parkin, you'll no say anything aboot the bacon?'

I suppose that there is a turning point in everyone's life—or a T-junction, perhaps, where you can go one way or the other. Mine came when I left university and had to choose between practical farming (working my way up through management and into a tenanted farm which was still possible then) or agricultural journalism. The lure of the land and livestock was strong; but so was that of Fleet Street and the typewriter. I chose the typewriter and have never regretted it. The editor of *The Farmers Weekly* had offered me a job at £750 a year, which my tutor told me was more than a lecturer at Reading was getting. A chum of mine who went down at the same time, with no agricultural background but with a lot of ambition, is now farming 3,500 acres (most of it rented) in Northamptonshire and must be worth a million. But my decision was a conscious one, made in the knowledge that it was a crossroads and one which has given me thirty years of excitement and fulfilment. To sit in front of a typewriter and watch the words come up and then to see them in print, or to hold a microphone under someone's nose and then to hear it broadcast are feelings which have to be experienced to be appreciated.

So I went back to the hurly-burly of *The Farmers Weekly* in the overcrowded, pulsating offices in Shoe Lane. Before long I moved to the splendour of the new Hulton House in Fleet Street where, for a time, I had probably the best office in the whole of the Street because it was the only one which faced east towards Ludgate Hill and St Paul's. I started as a general reporter doing the rounds of the shows in the summer and the conferences in the winter and began to specialise in the more technical topics and to build up contacts at the research stations and experimental farms.

During this time we were keen rivals of the *Farmer and Stockbreeder*, the other weekly, and we would go to almost any lengths to beat each other. One day I was in a pub having a quick lunch when I heard two farmers discussing a piece of mine which I had literally risked my neck over, having driven much further and much faster to get the copy back than I should have in order to beat the opposition. 'Did you see that piece this week?' he was saying. 'I think it was in the *Stockbreeder* . . .' I think we do, sometimes, go over the top to get a story first although once you tell a journalist it does not matter if the opposition beats him it is like telling a doctor it does not really matter if he saves life.

I referred there to driving back from an assignment but a car was one of the luxuries which had to be earned. Until you joined the lucky few with a company car it was a case of public transport and hope to find a taxi the other end. As many of the locations were in remote spots where cabs were few and far between, this meant that getting to and from a story was often more difficult than covering it. I remember once, in the days before I had persuaded the Editor that I needed a car, being sent to a grass-drying demonstration on a farm near Harrietsham in Kent. I took the train to Maidstone and found a bus to Harrietsham but was still a mile or two from the farm with the event due to start at any moment. The local garage failed to furnish a taxi but did point me in the direction of the farm and I started walking, hoping for a lift. Sure enough, along came a coke lorry which responded to my hitch-hiker's thumb. 'You're in luck, mate,' the driver told me, 'that's the farm we're going to. But you'll have to hop up on the back.' We drove into the yard a few minutes later to find the Ministry adviser standing on a trailer surrounded by fifty or sixty farmers and saying: 'Well, the *Farmers Weekly* chap's not here but we'd better make a start.' I gave a somewhat embarrassed wave from the top of the load of coke destined for the grass drier. 'Here I am,' I shouted. Someone gave me a hand down, I dusted myself off and got out my notebook.

One of the attractions of the media is that you never stop learning. The longer you spend in the press, radio or television the more you understand their limitations; which is one of the reasons why I never like to dogmatise about the communications business. For instance, you can be too early with a story. I realise now that one or two of my 'scoops' were published ten years too soon, like the one on the impact of freeze drying on farming. I should think that only half a dozen people were interested in it when it was published and they probably already knew all about it. Some of the features which I wrote for the *FW* were, in retrospect, ego trips for me, the photographer, the art editor or the paper itself and were of little practical use to the reader. This was brought home to me once after I had knocked out a short article about building a pole barn which brought a flood of enquiries whereas an ambitious series called 'Farming's Share in the Spoils of Power' about the application of radioactive chemicals to agriculture brought virtually no reaction (although it was listed in a scientific publication as 'a popular survey' which showed that not only farmers read the *FW*).

While covering the British Association meeting in Bristol for the paper I bumped into a BBC mogul in a bar who over a drink asked me whether I had ever done any broadcasting. The following week found me at Bush House recording a piece for an overseas programme which in turn led to several years of free-lance broadcasting, both for home and overseas, while still working at *The Farmers Weekly*. (I stick to its old title; it did not drop the definite article until after I had departed.) Then one day I noticed that the BBC was looking for an agricultural producer, saw it as a short cut to becoming editor of a 'paper' and was appointed.

EIGHT

Resisting the Pressures

By the time I reached the BBC in 1960 I had traversed the nursery slopes of bribery and corruption. Alas, I was never to see the foothills, let alone the peaks, mainly I suspect because they simply do not exist in the agricultural media to any extent. It is difficult to get too commercial about sheep or sugar beet and one of the agreeable aspects of my job is working for the most part with pleasant, honest folk. The double-dealers and arm-twisters either have not been attracted into the farming world or have quickly done a bunk on discovering that the pickings were not very good.

However, I do remember meeting an extremely indignant machinery correspondent in the days when I worked for *The Farmers Weekly*. He had been to the demonstration of a new tractor and had had to leave early as it was press day. When he said goodbye the PR man from the machinery firm handed him an envelope telling him it contained some notes which he might find useful. Thinking it was more details about the brake horse power or hydraulics of the machine he had been looking at, he opened the packet up on the train. It did contain notes as the man had said—twenty-five £1 ones, a lot of money in those days. He took the money straight to the editor who got on to the managing director of the firm involved. There was an almighty row and a fulsome apology from the PR man who explained it away by saying he had just come from the motor trade where it was standard practice. That was a long time ago and things in the motor trade may well have changed now.

My first brush with bribery's near neighbour, reward for a favour, came after I had had my very first signed piece in the paper. It was an article about a farmer who had won a national milk award with his Shorthorns. Shortly afterwards he sold the herd and a month or two later I happened to be passing his farm so decided to drop in and do a bit of reader-research. He was very welcoming. 'That article of yours,' he said; 'I reckon it put about two thousand pounds on the value of the cows when we sold them.'

The trouble with inflation is that it ruins any story which involves money, but you would be safe in adding another nought to that figure to bring it up to present values.

'I'd like to reward you,' he went on.

Oh dear, I thought. Here it comes. What I have been fearing, and so soon too.

'Come into the orchard,' he said. Worse and worse I thought, he does not want anyone to see. But I need not have worried. He led me over to a plum tree and demanded my cap. He then got down on all fours and, rummaging round in the long grass, filled it with over-ripe and wasp-damaged fruit.

'There you are,' he said as he handed it over. 'I just wanted you to know that I appreciated it.'

Farmers' inherent meanness has saved a great deal of mutual embarrassment in our line of country. They do not want to offer and we do not want to accept. But they will often try to extract the maximum advantage from a situation as happened to me when I was doing an interview with a daffodil grower. The story was about how he fitted daffodils into a general farm rotation, and very interesting it was and very good he was in front of the microphone. On our way round, before starting the interview, he showed me a packing shed full of bulbs and declared: 'All these are for sale.' Thinking I could do with some I asked him how much. 'Two-fifty a bag,' he replied. I told him I would like a bag when I left and we went on round the farm. We recorded the interview and as I was putting the equipment in the car he said 'Oh, your daffs,' and disappeared to fetch them. 'How much?' I asked, making it clear that I wanted to pay.

'Three pounds.'

'Three pounds? I thought you said they were two-fifty.'

'Ah, these are special ones,' he said and gave me a huge wink. I was getting in the car when he asked whether I could possibly give his telephone number as well as the full address when we broadcast the piece and say that he always had bulbs for sale. I told him I thought it extremely unlikely.

Nothing daunted, as I was driving off he banged on the roof of the car with his hand. I stopped.

'I wonder whether, when you introduce the interview, you could say "Home of the Trotter Herd of Pedigree Large White Pigs",' he shouted.

I must say the daffodils did us proud and still grace the entrance to my house although I am certain they were not 'special'. I think he just took me for a mug.

What started as a discussion on how we in the media resist pressures from various quarters seems to be turning into a history of farmers' cupidity and yet the two are very closely connected. You see, if farmers were not so parsimonious we might be open to a lot more temptation. Let me make it quite clear that the last thing which we in the media want or expect is any kind of inducement or reward for the work we do, much of which is by its nature of great benefit to the farming community. Yet the lack of appreciation for our efforts is often equalled only by the demand for further efforts.

Some years ago there was a huge glut of apples. Best Cox's Orange Pippins were selling for three old pence a pound while the, then, newly imported French Golden Delicious were making one shilling and ninepence. We had not yet joined the Common Market, so owed no vestige of a market to the French apple grower and we were undergoing one of our worst balance of payments situations. In any case the Cox's that year were an infinitely better apple than the intruder by any standards—so it seemed a good idea and in the interests of both the consumer and the producer to give the situation some publicity. The National Farmers' Union collaborated willingly in finding a convenient farm for us to film at and the idea was to do a three- or four-minute film pointing out that the Great apple-buying British public was paying seven times as much money as it need for an inferior imported article.

On my way to the location I bought (at my own expense) a couple of pounds of Golden Delicious and we decided to feed these into the grader so that they would appear, along with the Cox's, at an appropriate moment in the film. I was to start with a piece to camera and begin that by taking a huge bite out of a lovely rosy Cox. I ought to explain that the packhouse was stacked to the roof with bushel boxes of apples. The yard was full of them, so were all the buildings and there was a lorry loaded with apples which nobody wanted.

The camera whirred, I bit my apple and started my piece. Soon the Golden Delicious would tumble down the grader and I could declare the superiority of the home-grown product. The farmer and his son looked pleased. It was something which would do everyone some good. We would soon shift some of those Cox's!

'Cut,' shouted the director. 'It's no good. Grader's making too much noise. You'll have to move round a bit.'

We got ready to start again and I asked the farmer for another apple to bite.

'But you've already had one,' he gasped.

'I know, but I've bitten this one.'

'Well, can't you bite from the other side?' he asked. He went into a huddle with his son and grudgingly produced another apple.

But if farmers are too stingy to try it on there are plenty of others keen to bend a producer's ear. The range includes commercial people who have things to sell and want you to help sell them as well as bodies like the NFU who wish to influence the government, the public or other organisations and are looking for aid in that direction. The BBC's accolade is still valued and one has to be very circumspect.

Having said that, I have to react to some of the hundreds of handouts and invitations which land on my desk every week or there would be no programmes. And obviously in doing so I am bound to publicise someone's views or interests in the process. You cannot shrug off responsibility and I have no time for the broadcaster or journalist who excuses an error of judgment by saying that it is unlikely to have influenced anyone. If he believes that, why is he bothering with the job?

I have found that the best guide in these matters is common sense. The BBC has a system of 'reference up'. No one tells me, as a producer, what to put in programmes but if I want advice there is always someone to consult. However, you cannot rely on other people's counsel all the time. In fact I have found it necessary to refer up on only a handful of occasions in nearly twenty-five years as a producer and these have been delicate political or legal issues.

In practice we do not seem to have a lot of trouble, but I am lucky with a programme like *On Your Farm* which goes out this Saturday and next Saturday and the Saturday after. If I have allowed someone to sway me too far with their views (and that may well be a respectable body such as the Countryside Commission or the Consumers' Association) we can put it right the following week and many of our best items have arisen as a reaction to a complaint.

Whoever said that there is no such thing as a free lunch certainly hit the nail smack on the head. No one lunches anyone just for the fun of it, or perhaps I should say no one lunches a BBC producer just for the fun of it. Or hardly anyone. Because I did have one occasion which left me non-plussed. The head of one of Oxford's richest colleges asked me to lunch. I explained that it would be difficult to go to Oxford solely for that purpose. Could I get in touch next time I was going to be in the area and see if he was free? I did and he was.

He met me at the porter's lodge and took me to a small but lively drinks party and introduced me all round. We then proceeded to a quite superb lunch which I was assured was the daily fare. We talked about my programme and his college until about quarter past two when he excused himself but said that perhaps I might care to spend an hour or so with the college's estates bursar. He, in turn, was equally charming and we spent some time in the comfort of his office while he told me all about the agricultural land owned by the college and showed me the rent books, making no secret of the rents being paid by tenants, some of whom were household names in farming circles.

I was beginning to wonder where it was all leading. It had to be leading somewhere. No one entertains BBC producers simply to pass the time. I have always found it a good idea when one is not sure where one is heading to get in first. So I suggested that there was a good programme there. How an Oxford college managed its land. The estates bursar threw up his hands in genuine horror. No, no, no. That was not the idea. Nothing like that. Just thought I might be interested. Anyway, how about some tea?—and he rang the bell.

I stepped out into the darkening streets of Oxford half an hour later marvelling that there are still people who can indulge themselves in lunching someone who interests them. The college head – I had better not call him the provost or warden or whatever, it might identify the place – was a regular listener to *On Your Farm* and just, on a whim, wanted to meet the chap who produced it.

But, as I say, the general rule is that there is no such thing as a free lunch—and lunch here stands for anything. My general rule is that while I do not mind accepting invitations which include other journalists, I am extremely wary to the point of almost always saying no to an invitation from a commercial firm addressed to me alone. You may say that this does not speak highly of my judgment. My answer to that is that to drink someone else's wine is to incur an obligation, however small, and it is an obligation I would rather not have. To share it with others is in my view an entirely different thing and virtually removes any obligation. Fortunately most public relations and press officers appreciate this and in any event find it cheaper and more convenient to lobby a bunch of journalists than to do so individually.

Many of the foreign trips which I have enjoyed over the years have been organised by commercial firms, foreign governments or other institutions. If I do a programme as a result of one of these trips, although I am under no compulsion to do so, I make a point of saying so over the air. You may think that this gives whoever arranged the tour exactly the publicity he is seeking. It certainly gives them a mention but it also makes it perfectly clear why I went wherever it was and leaves me free to report as fairly as I am able.

Deciding whether to accept an invitation to go on a trip of this sort is not an easy thing, especially in my case where I, as editor, am making a decision to send me as reporter. I have often envied the journalist who is sent by his paper. If the trip turns out to be less fruitful than expected he simply goes back and says there was nothing in it (although there are very few jaunts where a keen journalist cannot find a story of some kind).

The whole thing starts with a letter or telephone call from the press officer of the firm or organisation concerned. It might be a chemical firm wanting to demonstrate the use of its sprays, the organisers of a foreign show trying to stimulate interest or a government which feels its farmers are being treated unfairly. Whatever the subject I should want to know what it was going to cost, how long it was going to take and what we were likely to get out of it in terms of material for broadcasting. Most people responsible for arranging trips of this kind have the sense to realise that if they are simply going to take a group of journalists across the Channel to see a combine factory they are not likely to have a very big party, because that is a story which is worth about one picture and a caption. So they will perhaps fix up visits to a couple of farms, a research station and, possibly, a meeting with a Minister or president of a farmers' union. At this stage the prospect begins to look interesting.

Often the fringe activities are more productive than the main purpose of the trip. I sometimes feel rather sorry for the poor press officer who sees his carefully laid plans going awry. No one seems to want to interview his managing director; they are all more interested in a peasant farmer who has crossed a Charolais with a Dexter on one of the holdings they visited. I remember a visit to Ulster laid on by the Northern Ireland government which coincided with the breaking of a big story on butter smuggling between the North and the South. In vain did the chairman of this or that creamery try to tell us about co-operative cheese-making. All we were interested in was who was making what out of butter. A trip to the States was similarly distorted by the great soya bean saga some years ago, I recall. I often wonder what post mortems must take place following some of these excursions where for the organisers the whole point of the exercise has somehow been lost. Press and public relations officers must be a long-suffering lot as they keep coming back for more. A lot of them, of course, are ex-journalists who have swapped independence for a fatter salary cheque and so know what to expect.

Occasionally the laugh is on us as it was once in Iowa when

I held the bus up while I got an interview with a farmer's wife on a farm we had just been round. She had done most of the talking during the visit and, while it had absolutely nothing to do with the main purpose of the trip, I felt there was a good interview there. It turned out to be the shortest interview I have ever done. I explained what I wanted, told her about the programme and its audience and asked her for her name and address while I 'took some level', in other words made sure I was holding the microphone in the right place and the machine was properly adjusted. I was just about to ask the first question, when she broke in with her slow flat mid-West voice: 'Do you mean to tell me that anything I say into that microphone will be broadcast on the BBC, coast to coast?'

'That's right,' I said, cheerfully.

'Oh,' she managed to mutter. And that was all I got out of a woman who ten minutes earlier had been standing on an upturned bucket addressing twenty strangers.

I am never very popular with my fellow journalists on these occasions because, at some stage, I have to get down on tape what they have already got down in their notebooks and often hold up proceedings as a result. But that is one of the factors I have to bear in mind when deciding whether to accept one of these invitations. I also consider who else is going (might there be a fellow journalist whom I can use as an interviewer or reporter?) and, if the destination is some non-English-speaking country, will there be anyone there with really good English to interview? Believe me, at quarter past seven on a Saturday morning, it *has* to be really good English if you do not want your audience turning over and going back to sleep.

Just to return to my point about referring in the programme as to how one came to be in Denmark, Portugal or Saskatchewan I personally regard this as an essential part of the business of accepting invitations of this kind. Not all my colleagues would agree. An example of how it can work to everyone's advantage might help here. A few years ago John Deere, the firm which makes among other things very large tractors, flew a group of agricultural journalists across the Atlantic to see some American farming. In the course of the trip I got several good interviews with men farming large acres with little labour—in one case a farmer and son running two thousand acres on their own. Obviously it was in the firm's interest to have a story like that featured but equally it made a fascinating piece in itself. But I still thought it necessary to start by saying 'Last week I was in the United States on a trip organised by John Deere . . .'. This has the dual effect of giving the firm the credit for having arranged it all but, more important, of making it clear *why* I was there. In other words I did not go just because I thought that the idea of farmers running large acreages with few men and huge machinery was desirable and therefore worth spending the BBC's money crossing the Atlantic to investigate but that here was an interesting trip with a story which I knew would prove thought-provoking.

The BBC's attitude to advertising is something which has undergone a profound though gradual change over the last quarter of a century. When I joined the Corporation it was still thought inadvisable to say 'Cellophane' and there was no such thing as a Thermos—it was a vacuum flask, if you don't mind. Fergusons were 'grey tractors'. Nowadays, although the Corporation has its code of conduct, we see the names of commercial firms punched up as captions every time a horse jumps at Wembley, and conductor James Loughran jokingly offering to hire out the back of his dress suit for advertising at the Proms.

Meanwhile, it is amazing how long the old BBC attitude to advertising has persisted in the minds of the listening and participating public. How often one hears in a phone-in programme someone say 'I know I can't mention the name' of the most trivial everyday item and I find a general expectation that trade names will not be used although, of course, in some cases a programme may be valueless unless they are. Again I find that our old friend common sense is as good a guide as any. It certainly seems to have kept me out of trouble without having to devise non-commercial euphemisms for everything. By and large the only time we get complaints seems to be when someone's product has been maligned, or the manufacturers feel it has. I cannot recall a single case in nearly fifteen hundred programmes when we have been censured for giving someone unfair publicity.

'Are you leaned on,' I am often asked, 'by people who do not want things broadcast,' because of course part of our usefulness lies in airing subjects which some folk would prefer to leave unexposed. I am not suggesting that we get involved too often in the *Checkpoint* type of incident where Roger Cook is manhandled downstairs to accompanying bangs, thuds and squeaks from his tape recorder before someone pulls out the microphone lead. The worst case I can remember was where one of two men taking part in a programme which I was chairing put his hand over the microphone. As it was a live transmission it did look nasty for a moment or two but fortunately it was an omni-directional mike and I was able to keep up a conversation with the other chap until he gave up trying to stop the discussion. It was a half-hearted attempt anyway—a symbolic protest at the line the debate was taking.

People do seem to have an enormous respect for the BBC. It never ceases to astonish me that contributors do not get up and walk out of the studio or challenge the interviewer more often. It is not an easy situation to deal with in a live programme as Kenneth Harris must have found once when George Brown (as he then was) turned on him, or when Defence Secretary John Nott walked out on Robin Day.

But I digress. The question was: 'Do we have pressure applied to keep things off the air,' and the answer, in my experience, has to be in the negative.

The usual form of protest from someone who does not want a topic featured is to refuse to take part in a programme and, sometimes, as far as he is able, persuade others not to take part. This in itself, while perhaps weakening a discussion of the subject, does not necessarily prevent its taking place. There is usually someone else who will take part or, as a producer, I have the option of presenting the argument through a journalist. If the worst comes to the worst, I can proffer only one side of the case while making it clear that the Spaghetti Growers' Association declined to take part. This must seem like dealing the producer all the best cards but unless he plays them wisely and responsibly neither he nor his programme is likely to have a long run.

I quite often get taken to task by those in high places for

tackling subjects which they would rather leave untouched – at least for the moment – but almost always after the programme has been broadcast. The President of the National Farmers' Union was extremely angry when we devoted a whole edition of *On Your Farm* to the controversial issue of farm tenancies and made the fact quite clear to me—but only after the programme had gone out. It was a subject on which the NFU had allowed itself to get wrong-footed and he did not want the ground worked over in public, particularly as it was the Saturday before the Union's AGM. He knew the programme was taking place because one of his lieutenants was contributing but I am certain that it would never have crossed his mind to ring me up and try to have the programme scrubbed.

Sometimes, of course, one can be argued out of a decision to deal with a topic but that is all part of the programme-making process when one is in the course of taking soundings and does not come under the heading of receiving pressure. Very occasionally someone will ask you to keep something specific out of a programme. I remember some years ago going to Suffolk to do one of our breakfast programmes with Jim Prior on his farm. He had not long been made Minister of Agriculture by Mr Heath somewhat to his surprise and, like his master, was flexing his muscles and making threatening noises about militancy and so on. It was being rumoured that he was making plans to cut the National Agricultural Advisory Service which came under his Ministry and, since things seemed to be going rather well at breakfast, we thought we would push our luck and ask him if he had made up his mind where the axe would fall. Much to our surprise he gave us chapter and verse; so many poultry advisers were for the chop, so many this, so many that.

While all this had been going on, his Press Officer, Terry Dawes, who was then guiding his fifth minister through the minefield of the media, had been sitting in the corner looking extremely unhappy. When it was all over he came up and said: 'Very good, Minister; very good indeed. I just wonder whether it was perhaps wise to spell out the cuts in the NAAS, at this stage.'

'Oh, perfectly all right,' said Mr Prior in his hearty way. 'Perfectly all right. No worries about that at all.'

We then had to drive at top speed the long journey back to Birmingham in order to arrive in time to tidy up the programme and dub on the signature tune. But as we sped along I was buoyed up by the fantastic scoop we had on the tape on the seat behind me. When we reached the old Broadcasting House in Carpenter Road an anxious commissionaire came out to meet me. Would I telephone the Permanent Secretary at the Ministry of Agriculture immediately?

Of course, I guessed what had happened. As we were driving hell for leather to Birmingham, Terry Dawes was doing the same towards London and his boss.

'Look,' he said. 'I don't like having to do this but I really don't think it's a good idea for these advisors to be told that they've got the sack by listening to *On Your Farm* on a Saturday morning. Don't you agree? I wonder if you could take it out?'

I said I would listen to it but in my heart I knew that he was right and that it would have to go. We managed to keep most of the Minister's challenging remarks but left out the detail of the cuts. But if the Permanent Secretary had not telephoned, I cannot say what I would have done.

A lot of the pressures which affect *On Your Farm* are applied at one stage removed, so to speak. People do not lean on me as producer but they do lean on the folk who have been invited to take part in a programme. This explains why some of the interviews and discussions lack the edge you might expect. The chap assured me he would say it when we talked about it on the telephone, but by the time he got into the studio someone had nobbled him. Not necessarily threatened him; nothing as sinister as that. No, just persuaded him it was not a very good idea, not in the best interests, old boy, you know the form. It can have a disastrous effect on a programme. I had a pharmacist not long ago prepared, nay eager, to talk about his relationship with the drugs firms and vets and their interrelationship. He wanted to let it all hang out. That was at half past eleven in the morning. By half past two when we recorded the piece it was a totally different story. Persons unknown had got at him in the meantime—the vets; a drugs firm; his professional body; his solicitor; his wife? I do not know. All I do know is that it completely unbalanced the programme and must have left listeners wondering why I had invited him to take part.

Yes, there are pressures applied to those of us who work in the media. Of course there are. Some subtle and some not so subtle. But in spite of its increasing complexity, the agricultural field is probably as free from them as any. We try to recognise them and to resist them. It helps if you always buy your own turkey at Christmas.

NINE

Underneath the Archers

In my earlier days as a producer of agricultural programmes I adopted a positive hands-off policy towards the world's longest-running radio serial, *The Archers*. Tony Shryane, the producer from its start in 1951 until he retired in 1978, was kind enough to invite me to all the parties – and there were several as ten years and then twenty years were clocked up – and suggested in his charming oblique way that some mention in *On Your Farm* would not come amiss. But I just had the feeling that fact and fiction would not mix happily. Then one day in 1972, after Godfrey Baseley's abrupt and unwilling departure, I found myself heavily involved. Would I, asked Jock Gallagher, Pebble Mill's dynamic Network Editor, Radio, and the man with ultimate responsibility for the programme, keep an eye on the agricultural side for a month or two until suitable arrangements could be made? I agreed and apart from six months in 1976 when a colleague gave me a breather I have remained the programme's Agricultural Story Editor and am now by far the longest-serving member of the production team.

The fears I had of being closely involved in a weekly programme about real agriculture and a daily one about an imaginary farming family have proved groundless. I cannot honestly claim that *On Your Farm* has benefited from the arrangement – its producer has had to spend far too much time in Ambridge – but I am confident that *The Archers* has profited from the connection. Not that there is any direct link; far from it, apart from an *On Your Farm* breakfast session to mark the thirtieth anniversary of this remarkable programme. (This, incidentally, was recorded in Pebble Mill's Studio Three where with the aid of sundry physical and electronic props our audio staff is able to conjure up Ambridge in all its guises from Lakey Hill to the Grundys' kitchen and from

Hollowtree piggery to The Feathers in Borchester.) But I am sure it must be an advantage to have guiding the affairs of Brookfield and Home Farm someone who is in constant touch with farmers and farming in the everyday world.

Then why, you might ask, is the agriculture of Ambridge not as sharply defined and up to date as that of *On Your Farm*? Why do the farmers who chat about their affairs on Radio 4 at five past seven each evening not sound like the ones you hear at quarter past seven on a Saturday morning? Why the difference, if the same chap is involved in both programmes? The answer is that the people you hear in *On Your Farm* are practising farmers risking their own money, making real decisions and getting horny hands in the process. What you hear in *The Archers* is not just one stage removed or even two; it is at least four stages removed and I often think that it is a miracle that it sounds as convincing as it does.

The first point to remember is that we start not with actual farmers but with my conception of them and their situations. However accurate these may be after forty years of rubbing shoulders with them it is not quite the same thing. The next point is that I then have to convey this secondhand conception to the script writers whose job it is to incorporate it in their scripts along with equally convincing interpretations of Sid Perks, Jack Woolley and Mrs P. Then, with *On Your Farm*, we have the immense advantage of broadcasting the programme either live or at worst only twenty-four hours after it was recorded whereas *The Archers* shoulders the everlasting burden of being written three months before it goes on the air; there is no chance of referring to the actual weather or the markets or what the Minister of Agriculture said yesterday—all the things which breathe so much life into the Saturday programme. Lastly, whatever I manage to convey to the writers and however skilful their dialogue it still has to be spoken by actors who again are not farmers and sometimes do not sound much like them.

There have been several script editors since Godfrey Baseley's day, none of whom would claim to know a great deal about agriculture. The first of them, the likeable Malcolm Lynch, had worked on *Coronation Street* and he certainly made things happen in Ambridge. Although I bent over backwards to help him agriculturally there was a fundamental rift in our attitudes. For example to me a bull is something essential to getting cows in calf; to Malcolm it was associated more with china shops. So when, at his insistence, a bull named Horace was introduced into the series it was mainly so that it could break loose and terrorise the village. (After Malcolm's departure, Horace was to everyone's surprise found to be impotent and had to go for mincemeat.) I remember Malcolm poking his friendly face round the door of my office one afternoon and saying: 'Give me the name of a sheep disease.'

'A sheep disease,' I mused. 'What sort of sheep disease?'

'Don't mind,' he replied. 'Give me a name.'

I rattled off a few of the shepherd's nightmares—braxy, gid, pulpy kidney, swayback, twin lamb, blackleg, joint ill and so on. When I got to orf his face lit up. 'Orf,' he said, 'that sounds good. How do you spell it?'

'O–r–f,' I answered, 'but hang on a moment.' It was too late. He had gone to kill off half someone's flock with orf, an unpleasant, unsightly disease but not one which, I think, has ever proved fatal.

But while Malcolm and I had some good-natured disagreements over things of this kind, the overall beneficial effects of his reign over Ambridge were showing up in increased listening figures.

His successor, Charles Lefeaux, looked exactly like Sir Thomas Beecham and could behave almost as irascibly but his three years as script editor were, for me, the most agreeable of my time with the programme. He was a professional to his fingertips after many years in radio drama and conducted the monthly script conferences in an extremely businesslike fashion at a brisk trot. He died while walking on his beloved Hampstead Heath at the age of seventy; lucky for him but less so for his charming wife. There were the barest minimum of changes in the writing team during Charles' reign and I would regularly take the writers to visit farms which had some relevance to the development of the Ambridge holdings. I gave up the practice when the team began constantly to change since few of the writers seemed particularly interested. Why bother to understand farming, seemed to be the attitude, when you have an Agricultural Story Editor to supply all the stuff in note form?

Oddly enough, the only time I ever threatened to leave the team was during Charles Lefeaux's period although I must admit to having been tempted to walk out of script conferences several times since. But on this particular occasion one of the writers wanted to put Shula Archer on the pill, at the age of sixteen. With three daughters of my own in their 'teens, or nearly there, I protested. It is happening, I was told, so why not let it happen in Ambridge? My argument was that there was all the difference in the world between a practice taking place and our giving it *The Archers*' 'seal of approval' and that to do so in this case would have daughters the length and breadth of the country, including mine perhaps, saying: 'But, Mummy, even Shula Archer's taking it.' The writers were more or less agreed, Charles was equivocal and I was adamant and, although it could in no way be said to be an agricultural point, I won the day. Mind you, from events which took place subsequently in Ambridge, it might be inferred that Shula was taking precautions, but that was different from making a big issue out of it. The scenes were carefully written to include an element of doubt.

Although each member of the team is on his or more likely these days her own when it comes to writing a script the general story lines are hammered out and agreed at monthly conferences attended by the writers, myself and William Smethurst who since 1978 has combined the role of producer and script editor and has a habit of flinging ideas around like confetti. He has one of the most inventive minds of anyone I have ever met and will run off a whole catalogue of possible developments of a situation while the rest of the team sits silent. His written story line, purportedly a note of what was agreed at the script meeting, is peppered with further inspired suggestions. It is a pity in some ways that he ever gave up writing the scripts himself. Meanwhile the monthly conferences have not always been as happy as they once were. There was one six-month period when they turned into bitter and cynical affairs with some members of the team apparently more interested in changing the face of Ambridge to conform with their own concepts of society than in understanding what makes a rural community tick; in campaigning for rape crisis centres or one-parent families or women's rights rather than getting to terms with what is involved in growing a good crop of sugar beet or rearing a bunch of calves.

Having said that I must add that no decision is taken lightly and I think that an eavesdropper would be astonished at the general degree of responsibility displayed. Whether or not to give a character a miscarriage, for example, is chewed over at great length and Clarrie's near mishap did not result in her losing the baby only because it was realised that it would come at a time when the Princess of Wales was due to give birth and that the resulting pathos would be too great for the listening public. On another occasion a planned miscarriage had to be abandoned because the actress playing the part had a real one. Miscarriages, in case it might be thought that *The Archers* is obsessed with them, are like broken engagements. They possess the dual advantage of providing moments of high drama while at the same time prolonging the action. In a daily soap opera you do not want your babies to arrive too quickly or your eligible maidens to marry off too soon.

William Smethurst's constant search for new writing talent has brought enormous headaches for me. Something like twenty writers have had a go at *The Archers* since I became enmeshed and although the team now seems to have settled down a bit there are still seven or eight involved, a far cry from the first ten years when two men, Edward J. Mason and Geoffrey Webb, wrote every script. The present team is planned to be rotated in two groups of four writers, each of whom writes one week in four over a period of six months. Thus none of them, or so it seems to me, has the commitment to become thoroughly familiar with the Ambridge agricultural scene. Farming is not something which can be taken in like a hand-out from some trendy pressure group or other. I have been absorbing it through every pore for forty years and would not claim a proper understanding. So what chance does a townee living in a large conurbation and writing perhaps only six scripts a year stand, however intelligent he or she may be? But in spite of all I have said I have to admit that William's search for excellence has paid off in some ways (even if it has been partly at my expense). In terms of pure radio drama the scripts are probably better than they have ever been.

The trouble is that with any programme, and especially with one like *The Archers*, every year makes success harder to achieve. I appreciate this with *On Your Farm*. No producer wants his programme to go downhill. To keep it on the level is extremely difficult to achieve since this exposes it to this risk of decline. So you try to keep it on a slightly upward incline. Not an easy job as the years go by and with listeners so keen to make comparisons.

The original brilliance lay in the conception of *The Archers*, in the creation of Ambridge along with Dan and Doris, Phil and Chris, Jack and Walter Gabriel. That was Godfrey Baseley's achievement and no one can ever take it from him. Once the programme was invented, the first ten years must have been exciting but relatively easy. It was all new. No one had ever done it before (and television had only begun to nibble away at the audience). We are now into the fourth decade and virtually everything has been done before as someone is sure to remind us at every script meeting—if not by us then by *Coronation Street*. On the other hand we may be overlooking the fact that although some people have been listening for thirty years others may just have started and could still be as gripped by the birth of a calf as listeners to the first episode were way back in 1951.

What, you may be wondering at this stage, is the role of the Agricultural Story Editor apart from criticising the rest of the team? My job is to try and keep both the agricultural foreground and background on terms with reality and moving in the right direction. What began as a largely advisory job has taken on a more positive aspect over the years and I now supply the writers with a detailed brief on almost everything to do with farming in Ambridge. I suggest story lines and if these are agreed follow them up with carefully researched blow-by-blow notes. Those on Mike Tucker's TB breakdown, for example, extended to nine pages. I aim to feed everything in before the writers start in the hope that when the scripts are passed to me for editing they need little attention. There are both macro and micro aspects to be considered. Moving Mike Tucker into the Pounds' farm, for instance, forms part of the grander strategy, whereas dehorning calves at Bridge Farm comes into the latter category. But both need careful advice to the writers if the scripts are to sound convincing. I also supply the writers with a monthly diary telling them week by week what is likely to be happening on each of the major holdings—Brookfield (Phil Archer), Home Farm (Brian Aldridge), Bridge Farm (Tony Archer), Ambridge Farm (Mike Tucker) and occasionally Grange Farm (Joe Grundy). Although they are also supplied with the perpetual Ambridge Agricultural Calendar, which I devised some years ago, this needs pointing up in the light of annual or seasonal changes; as, for example, when Phil Archer started lambing a month earlier to try and take advantage of the higher lamb price.

Some of my proposals have altered the shape of Ambridge permanently. One of the first changes I urged was the splitting up of the over-large Bellamy empire of four thousand acres into several more reasonably sized holdings. This led to the establishment of the 1,500-acre Home Farm, which was plenty big enough for Ambridge, and paved the way for the introduction of Brian Aldridge, the well-breeched young man from the Home Counties whom Jennifer was to marry. I was responsible for the creation of the 100-acre Willow Farm (now sadly amalgamated) which filled a long-felt gap at the lower end of the farming spectrum enabling us to launch Tony Archer on his career and later to move Brookfield's cowman, Mike Tucker, into it and so give a farm worker a start on the farming ladder. It was also at my suggestion that we brought in a young apprentice, Neil Carter, who has proved to be one of the most consistently successful characters on the Ambridge scene.

In spite of the relentless effort to include agricultural material we are constantly being told that 'there's hardly any farming in *The Archers* these days' and asked 'why can't it be like it was twenty years ago?' An examination of the scripts of that period certainly does not bear out the comparison although it is true that the farming in Ambridge in those days was spelt out in capital letters whereas nowadays our writers weave it in less obtrusively. I must admit to feeling slightly sensitive to the charge in view of all the effort which I know goes into it. When the accusation was repeated at a meeting of the Central Agricultural Advisory Committee, the body which as its name suggests considers the whole of the BBC's agricultural output, I was spurred into doing a little research. I combed back through the previous eight months of *Archers'* output and discovered no fewer than thirty-eight significant agricultural stories some of them very long-running ones. Here is the list I presented to members of the Committee at its following meeting.

1. Mike Tucker tries to ensure that Bellamy's workers get redundancy pay. Principle and practice of redundancy pay discussed over several episodes.

2. Sale and split-up of Bellamy estate—a story with its ramifications running through the first half of the year. e.g.:

- 1,500 acres sold to industrialist who farms it in partnership with a Velcourt-type company; pros and cons of this sort of operation discussed at various levels.
- 1,500 acres sold to youngish farmer who has sold smaller acreage in Home Counties. His takeover of farm and plans for running it (cereals, sugar beet and oil-seed rape with sheep) are discussed in detail over long period.
- 1,000 acres kept by Bellamy for eventual transfer to his son. Difficulties of doing this, effect of Capital Transfer Tax, etc. discussed at length in many episodes.

3. Ken Pound's foot will not heal—opportunity to discuss, over a period, difficulty facing one-man farmer when he is ill.

4. Sale of Bull Farm—fifty acres on edge of village. Like many farms of this sort it is split up. Ten acres adjoining village are bought by a speculator who hopes one day to develop it. The house and five acres are sold to a commuter with horses whose family subsequently plays a part in story. Thirty-five acres are bought by Phil since it adjoins Brookfield. Land values related to returns from farming and uses to which he could put the land discussed over several episodes.

5. Betty Tucker decides to keep bees. Later she takes a swarm in Jill's garden.

6. Tony Archer loses three calves with scour. When he is short of cash he has to spend money on alterations to old buildings to cut out draughts.

7. Grundy lets a field for a pop concert (opportunity to discuss NFU's advice to farmers on this).

8. Pat Archer has to help Uncle Haydn out in garage at short notice. Her help at Willow Farm is missed by Tony.

9. Phil and Dan take stock of the previous farming year in detail (over two scenes). Opportunity to discuss fodder shortage, etc. in retrospect.

10. Phil and Dan discuss whether to increase herd from 90 to 120. Phil is in favour; Dan has misgivings but plan goes ahead.

11. Dan's ewes get twin-lamb disease due to his keeping them too short of expensive feed. A blow-by-blow account of the impact and treatment of this disease at a time when many farmers were suffering similarly.

12. Tony takes stock and discusses his plans for building up to 60 milkers by autumn. Cash flow difficulties force him to sell some heifers he had hoped to keep.

13. Tony and Pat decide they want a sideline. Various possibilities discussed over several scenes, including contract-rearing of pullets.

14. Phil's sows up to strength again after SVD outbreak of previous year. Discussion over several episodes of the advantages and disadvantages of minimal disease stock.

15. Development of Neil's 'new entrant' course forms a recurring theme. After working with Jethro (who finds it difficult to teach his skills) and in the dairy, he has a spell on the sheep and then with the pigs. Later he has to decide where to specialise (he decides on livestock) and whether to go to college for his final year of apprenticeship or to stay at Brookfield (he stays).

16. Dan Archer shoots a dog which is sheep worrying. Provides opportunity over several scenes to discuss new Animals Act.

17. Several Ambridge residents, at various times, state their determination to get more out of their kitchen gardens this year.

18. Phil is growing maize for the first time—mentions pros and cons of crop.

19. Dan and Phil discuss repairs and maintenance of their tackle. Agree to have it done at Haydn's garage (by Peter who used to do Bellamy's).

20. Two bullocks are nearly poisoned by eating rhododendrons (after Neil leaves a gate open). They recover after visit from vet.

21. Pat decides to try free-range poultry. Buying of second-hand equipment, installing hens, etc. over several scenes. Later a fox takes some.

22. Pat tries selling the eggs through the farm shop (which reopens after winter break) but Mary is afraid that free-range eggs will turn her own battery ones into a second-class commodity.

23. Phil becomes vice-chairman of the NFU branch; he tries recruiting new members.

24. Sinclair takes over the running of Bellamy's 1,000 acres, part of which is in hand and part let. Acting like a new broom he starts by putting the pressure on some of the tenants, keeping them up to the terms of their agreements.

25. In the wake of last year's tied cottage battle in Ambridge, which nearly ended in an eviction, and anticipating legislation following Labour Party manifesto, discussion takes place over several scenes in which both sides of the argument are aired again. During the process several characters realise that they, too, live in 'tied' accommodation including Tony and Pat, the vicar, the policeman and Sid and Polly at the Bull.

26. Metrication: the difficulties facing farmers and farm workers of coming to terms with metrication are discussed, during which the timing of the metrication of various aspects of the agricultural scene is referred to.

27. The Tuckers decide to keep goats. Various aspects of this are gone into in some detail over a number of episodes.

28. A topical insert in the first week of June features the effect of the unusual weather on crops and grass.

29. An elderly tenant on Bellamy's 1,000-acre estate tells Sinclair that he wants to retire and pass the farm on to his nephew. Sinclair says that, because of Capital Transfer Tax, this will not be possible—in order to maximise his concessions under the tax, Bellamy wants to take as much land in hand as possible (previous discussion between Lilian Bellamy and

Peggy Archer having explained CTT situation in this respect).

30. Various characters visit Royal Show.

31. Stacking bales in loft over calfhouse, Jethro falls through rotten floor and breaks a leg. The knock-on effects of this run for three months. Mike Tucker persuades Jethro to claim compensation; the Safety Inspector calls and threatens Phil with prosecution; extra labour has to be recruited at Brookfield for harvest.

32. Phil goes to see harvesting of oil-seed rape at Aldridge's farm. Aldridge describes pros and cons of growing this relatively new crop.

33. The student (non-agricultural) obtained at short notice to replace Jethro keeps doing things wrong—he runs into a gatepost and breaks the stub axle of one of the tractors just before harvest; next he puts calf-feed in the parlour hoppers; finally he tips 3–4 tons of corn in a neat swath across the field as he takes a load from the combine. His replacement, an agricultural student, is much more reliable.

34. Bobby Walters falls in the parlour and hurts his back. Sinclair has to take over the job at short notice and take his coat off.

35. Neil leaves a gate open in the piggery; two bunches of baconers fight, one is killed and another has to be taken to the slaughterhouse.

36. A few days later they develop erysipelas; an injection cures them but it reminds Phil that he has been neglecting his routine preventive measures.

In addition to the foregoing there have been countless smaller references to farming operations in the serial. These fall into three categories:

First, small incidents of the kind which form part of everyday life on farms, e.g.:

- calves get into kitchen garden and trample all seedlings in;
- electricity repeatedly goes off in parlour; turns out to be due to water being held up by cobwebs behind fuse-box.
- Tony is chain sawing; later comes into house with gumboots full of sawdust which he spreads round kitchen.

Second, routine jobs used as background for conversation,

giving authenticity to situation, often with sound effects, e.g.:

- changing teat cup liners;
- carrying out pregnancy diagnosis;
- earmarking calves;
- injecting for foul-in-the-foot.

Third, seasonal jobs usually mentioned in course of conversation at appropriate time of year such as lambing, drilling, top-dressing, harrowing, silage-making, and so on.

That does not seem to me to be a bad record for agricultural content over a period of eight months and I do not think that it has diminished since that inventory was drawn up in 1975.

It is a tribute to the series, although something of a nuisance at times, that so many people want to hear their special interests reflected in *The Archers*. Some of them fail to appreciate the three- to four-month gap which takes place between the discussion of the script and the transmission of the actual episode. (It is confusing enough for those of us involved who are simultaneously exposed to material at four different stages – initial discussion, editing the script, recording and then finally hearing it over the air – and often find difficulty in remembering the stage that any particular story line has reached.) The result is that I may be asked to put in a reminder that ewes must be dipped by the end of next week, for example, when next week's episodes have been recorded for five or six weeks and written three months ago. It is a matter of quiet satisfaction when I have already anticipated the situation and Phil and Brian have been recorded discussing that very subject.

However, what most of the individuals and organisations who approach us fail to realise is that we cannot simply *mention* things—that is not what radio drama is all about. Something has to happen. It is a pretty safe bet that if we succumb to pressure from, say, the Ladies Side Saddle Association to set up a branch in Borchester, then sooner or later someone is going to fall off a horse and the Association will almost certainly disapprove. A case to illustrate this took place some years ago in the days when Tony Archer was still unattached. I was under constant bombardment from the Institute of Agricultural Secretaries to bring a farm secretary into *The*

Archers. It did not seem an outrageous suggestion and eventually, after discussion at a script conference, we decided to cast a travelling secretary. I was immediately inundated with information from the Institute telling me what she should be doing, which course she should be going on, when the annual meeting was and so on. Meanwhile, the writers wanted more interesting action. You cannot have an eligible young woman abroad in Ambridge without something *happening*. And sure enough, one Friday afternoon she turns up at Willow Farm to do Tony's books. Tony has pulled the sofa up near the fire and she takes the hint. 'But what about the accounts?' he bleats as she makes for the sofa. 'Oh, bother the accounts' comes the reply, or something to that effect, followed by the well-known signature tune. I never heard again from the Institute and I just hope that in an alleyway one dark night I do not meet some of its members who feel that the integrity of their organisation was impugned.

More recently I was approached to give some publicity to the National Dairy Queen Competition. Again it was discussed at a script meeting, some mileage seen in it by some of the team and a decision made to go ahead. The organisers were delighted and deluged us with material covering every step from the initial entry form to the grand finale at Woburn in the autumn, anticipating no doubt that it would be the major theme of the Ambridge year. But not quite. Both Shula and Clarrie enter: Clarrie unexpectedly wins the initial heat but fortunately, since no one wanted to be lumbered with the story until October, it is discovered that because she is married she is ineligible and has to withdraw. How the organisers of the competition reacted, I do not know but I felt that this was a happy example of giving their event some publicity and *The Archers* several very nice scenes indeed without going over the top. Incidentally, it was a sign of the times that at the script conference at which it was decided to go ahead with the story only one of the writers was keen to handle it. The others felt that such contests violated their feminist principles.

'Are you going to mention Smithfield this year?' a friend of mine who was handling the publicity for the Royal Smithfield Show asked me two or three years ago.

'I don't know,' I said. 'I'll bring it up at our next meeting.' I did and the result was the coach trip to London organised by Sid Perks. Unfortunately for my chum it was not quite as straightforward as it looked. Sid starts to fix up the trip. Then there is not enough support, then it is on again, then it looks as if it will not take place. The suspense was too much for my friend who rang me up a week before the show (and ages after it had all been written and recorded, of course) and cried: 'For Pete's sake put me out of my misery. Does he take the ruddy coach or doesn't he?'

He had already achieved considerable publicity for the show by this time but obviously felt that the edge would be taken off this considerably if there were ultimately too few people from Britain's best-known farming village to fill Sid's coach.

William Smethurst, who as editor is subject to far more pressure than I am, showed me a letter one day from someone complaining that there were no coloured people in *The Archers*. 'Simple,' I told him. 'Tell them that in a village like Ambridge there just would not be any coloured folk. Full stop.' But that was too simple to satisfy William's impish sense of humour and he concocted a gem of a reply saying that there were in fact coloured people in Ambridge and it was a tribute to the skill of the script writers that it was not apparent who they were. Did the writer of the letter want them addressed as Rastus or Sambo? The writer of the letter was not amused and passed William's reply on to a women's lib magazine which printed it under the heading 'Smug Racism'.

Writing *The Archers*, which I have had a go at once or twice when there was a strong agricultural story running through the week, is nothing like as easy as it looks. It takes about ten days of solid hard work to produce five episodes. You cannot start too soon or you will not know what the previous week's writer has done with the characters and you dare not leave it too late as you have a deadline to meet. You start surrounded by pieces of paper giving details of everything from what Phil is likely to be doing on the farm that week to when Adam's school breaks up; from the anniversary of Grace Archer's death to which day Brian has to put the rams to his ewes. You have the general story line agreed at the previous script meeting into which you weave your own plots and sub-plots. And you have your own research to do; my last week involved speaking to, amongst others, an eye surgeon, a doctor, three farmers, a garage owner and someone from the Agricultural Training Board.

Perhaps the greatest constraint, apart from the time factor, is the limitation on the number of characters you can use. Thirty-two a week was the maximum the last time I wrote which means three episodes with six characters and two with seven. As most episodes usually have six or seven scenes this means that if you have Phil, Dan and Shula in scene one and Nelson, Mark and Jackie in scene two there is no way you can have Sid or Martha, Jennifer, Pat, Tony, Walter or anyone else that day. The other four or five scenes would have to include permutations of the characters in your first two scenes. Not that you would be likely to plan it that way but it explains why if you hear Colonel Danby or George Barford in scene one you are almost bound to hear them again before the episode is over. There is one blessed exception to this and that is Tom Forrest. He, or rather Bob Arnold the actor who has played him from the start, is on a permanent contract and can be used anywhere. He is the only character you can afford to have leave after saying only a couple of words or come in right at the end of a scene for a few lines. William Smethurst has described him aptly as the Greek chorus, hovering in the background, coming and going, carrying the gossip, never far away. The reason for limitation on characters is, of course, money. Actors are expensive though essential ingredients, like writers, producers, directors and agricultural story editors.

It is possible to create the impression of considerably more characters by subtle reference. Tony calls at Brookfield, for example, to see Phil who is out but who, by ingenious allusion in the script can almost become part of the cast for the evening. This necessary ploy is far from popular with the cast whose characters are frequently referred to to keep them 'alive' but who do not receive a contract. Few people would have realised that 'our Chris' did not take part in the series for a period of six months recently (I certainly did not until I met

Lesley Saweard, the actress who plays the part, in the lift at Pebble Mill). Someone has always just seen her or was going for a ride with her later. And the idle Higgs, Jack Woolley's chauffeur with his bottle-green uniform and fancy woman at Hollerton Junction, has never been cast. He exists totally in the listener's imagination.

Having worked out your week and how to achieve the impossible with only six or seven characters a day you then submit your cast list to the *Archers*' office only to face the possibility that one of the actors you need has suddenly gone 'non-available' – in other words is unwell, having an impromptu holiday or has landed a job in repertory or pantomime – causing a total re-think. Meanwhile carbon copies are arriving from the previous writer and as soon as you start writing you despatch copies to next week's writer. It is a creative production line with the same pressure in the studio. A fortnight's episodes are recorded in three concentrated days which means anything up to seventy scenes to be rehearsed and recorded complete with often elaborate sound effects. It is not surprising that tempers occasionally become frayed and it would be untrue to claim that we are always united. The actors complain from time to time about their lines and the writers now and then about the acting. The producer complains about the writers and the actors and no doubt all of them complain about the agricultural story editor. But in the end everyone pulls together to produce a programme which can still draw three million listeners and one which after thirty-odd years could still attract a record press turnout to the re-casting of Dan Archer.

Two films made to celebrate anniversaries of *The Archers* have given me a taste of what I suppose I have, wearing my other hat, been dishing out to people over the last twenty years. It was a curious sensation to be on the receiving end of a persuasive producer's tongue. Roger Mills was making a television documentary about the programme to celebrate its twenty-fifth birthday and came to see me about the agricultural aspects of it.

'I hear you take writers round farms from time to time,' he said. 'It would be nice to film them looking at the raw material.'

What we were in the habit of doing at that time was to visit a farm in the morning, have a ploughman's lunch at a local pub, often with the farmer and his family, and then hold a script conference in the pub in the afternoon. This was ideal for Roger enabling him to kill two birds with one stone—a farm outing and a script conference in one day's filming. The only snag was that the next visit was to be to a friendly landowner at his minor stately home. It was very much a one-off affair, intended to give the team an insight into an aspect of agriculture which was growing in importance—land ownership, the landlord–tenant relationship, Capital Transfer Tax and other issues which we were busy reflecting in the series through the break-up of the Bellamy estate and the creation of the Haydn Evans landlord–tenant partnership with Willow Farm. I was determined not to have the team filmed in a country house setting which would project quite the wrong image to anyone watching the programme. It was the first visit of this kind and almost certainly the last.

Roger pricked up his ears at the idea (as I am sure I should have done in his place). No, no, he assured me smoothly. They would not be interested in the country house as *such* but could I not see that there would be plenty of room for cameras, that sort of thing? The other location in which he was interested was the Royal Show—so colourful on television. Would I be taking the writers to the Royal? The answer was an emphatic and honest 'no'. It was the worst possible place for me to take them. With people who have difficulty in distinguishing between hay and straw the very last thing you want to do is to confuse them with concepts like 'tramlines' in cereals, baled silage and controlled oestrus. We should have Ambridge littered with new techniques which no one really understood, which lasted one episode and then had to be disposed of discreetly. To cut a long story short Roger *did* film at the country house and he *did* film the writers being shown round the Royal.

When we reached the country house for our meeting the camera crew was already there taking pictures of old family portraits and all the paraphernalia of gracious living with which I was anxious to avoid having the team associated. We sat round the long polished dining table and I whispered in

Charles Lefeaux's ear, 'Can I count on your support for *not* being filmed going out of the front door with a couple of gun dogs?' Charles agreed that it would be most undesirable. At least he gave a convincing impression of someone who thought it undesirable. Two hours later, by which time the silver, porcelain and other objets d'art had duly been filmed for use as cutaways – in addition to the meeting, of course – guess what happened. Very long pan from the edge of the park up to the house. Zoom in on front door as it opens and who should come out? Why, the landowner, Charles Lefeaux, Tony Shryane, four script writers, the agricultural story editor and two Labradors. The trouble with television is that pictures speak louder than words. No explanation in the commentary could possibly destroy the impression left in the viewer's mind of the link between the *Archers* team and stately homes. Ah well, no lasting harm done. Five years later we were doing it all again with Angela Rippon, although of course with a different producer and script editor and an entirely new writing team.

Some time ago I was seconded via the Commonwealth Fund for Technical Co-operation to the Fiji Government to try and help develop the country's agricultural broadcasting. Fiji's Prime Minister had been staying in London and had heard a number of our agricultural programmes and wanted to develop the same sort of service in his own country. Unfortunately I was able to help only to a limited extent because I came to the conclusion that what was wrong with the farming programmes in Fiji was that they were controlled by, produced by and presented by the Ministry of Agriculture's staff. My main recommendation was that responsibility should be handed over to the professional communicators at the Fiji Broadcasting Commission, working if necessary in close liaison with the Ministry of Agriculture. Due to the workings of internal politics this apparently was not a possible solution and I understand that the programmes are still being generated by the Ministry. The reason I bring this in here is because out of my visit was born the archetype of a Fiji *Archers*—not taking Ambridge to the South Seas but a truly homespun series with one major difference. There had to be two Dan Archers—one Fijian and the other Indian, to reflect the racial make-up of the country. Knowing how successful *The Archers* had been here over the years in disseminating information I had gone to Fiji armed with recordings and scripts of the series to find that there were individuals at both the university and FBC fostering similar objectives. My presence there was mainly that of a catalyst; the fact that I was there for a relatively short period encouraged everyone interested in the project to come together.

In a never-to-be forgotten day of excitement at the University of the South Pacific in Suva, the country's capital, sixteen of us met to discuss the idea—seven Indians, five Fijians and four Europeans (one of whom had been born in Fiji). The day started with a playback of an episode of *The Archers* and finished, miraculously, with a reading of the first four scripts of the new series. In between had come the enthusiastic adoption of the concept, agreement over the main objects of the programme, the creation of the central characters and location of Fiji's Ambridge, followed by the splitting up of the gathering into four writing teams, each including at least one Fijian and one Indian, and the actual writing of the opening quartet of scripts. These had all the freshness and drama of the early *Archers* days and each was complete with a gripping cliffhanger—a pig gone missing, a fire in the sugar cane, two young children adrift in a boat and the arrival of a portentous letter from the university. It was an incredible achievement in ten hours as well as being a remarkable example of group and inter-racial effort.

The aim of the new series, which they decided to call *Neighbours* was to produce a weekly fifteen minutes which would be compulsive listening through its sheer entertainment value and to use this constructively through the development of the story line to help build up good race relations, to slow down the drift to the towns, to discuss topical social issues and, of course, to put over new agricultural techniques. The characters and location had been chosen carefully with this in mind and although, from my description, this may appear to have been done somewhat hurriedly it ought to be explained that all of those at the initial workshop were people who had already given the matter some thought and had gone along with preconceived ideas which were then pooled. The two main characters – the twin Dan Archers – were Josefa Degai, a Fijian subsistence farmer who also did a spot of fishing and his neighbour and tenant the Indian sugar-cane farmer, Raja Ram. Both were married and by a careful manipulation of their children and parents we were able to give them potentially useful connections with the towns and islands. Sad to say, at the time of writing *Neighbours* has not yet gone on the air. Although far less ambitious than *The Archers*, like any radio drama it would be extremely complicated and expensive to mount, too much at present for FBC's limited resources, and will have to take its turn. But I have no doubt, based on the initial showing, that when the time is ripe the talent is there to bring it to fruition.

My feeling was that a responsible drama of *The Archers* type could do an immense amount of good in a developing country (and one without television but where every family has a transistor radio). After all *The Archers* was credited with having done much to get agriculture moving here in its earlier days, although I discovered that this was not the primary objective of the farmer who was credited with having first put up the idea in the late forties, Henry Burtt. I met Mr Burtt when I was doing a 'Taking the Pulse' edition of *On Your Farm* in Lincolnshire not long ago, hale and hearty at the age of ninety. He explained to me that what had been at the back of his mind in suggesting a programme about a farming family was not, as has always been generally supposed, to put new ideas over to the farming community but to create a better image of farmers in the eyes of the consuming and taxpaying public. That, I would say, the programme has undoubtedly done and Mr Burtt was even more far-sighted than we all thought, realising sooner than most the pressures which were to come as the farming fraternity became a smaller and smaller proportion of the electorate.

My own particular fantasy concerning *The Archers* is to see the programme written, recorded and broadcast on a daily basis, without the three-month delay with all that it entails. Imagine writing the episode every morning with the day's news and events for the characters to react to, the weather not as we imagine it to be in three months time but as it is – rain or sun – the livestock and produce markets with their ups and downs. And then to record it in the afternoon and transmit it soon afterwards. Of course, it would be far too expensive in terms of actors, writers, production staff and studios. But what a superlative programme it would be.

TEN

Auntie and Her Relations

Successful marriages these days are, sadly, becoming less common so that to have enjoyed not just one but two blissfully happy unions is to be blessed beyond belief. Especially when you consider that it is well over twenty years since I took a mistress as well and a very demanding one at that. I refer, of course, to the BBC which since the liaison began has seen far more of me than my wife has. The 'affair' has experienced the odd hiccup – what affair has not? – but at heart the Corporation and I suit each other like roast lamb and red-currant jelly and have enjoyed nearly a quarter of a century of what I sincerely believe to have been a symbiotic relationship.

A good friend of mine, not altogether innocent of intellectual snobbery, on hearing that I was to join the organisation stigmatised it as the embodiment of competent mediocrity. He was certainly correct about the competence. What other institution or company can claim to have delivered a consistently high-quality product onto the market, on time to the second, virtually without a break for as long as most of us can remember? The charge of mediocrity was, I assume, his way of reproaching the Corporation for failing to broadcast a round-the-clock output of Stockhausen and Berg, Anouilh and Brecht. At the same time I was told by a colleague who had worked for the BBC that 'Auntie' combined the most attractive elements of the theatre, Fleet Street, the senior common room and the civil service. (It is interesting to note that the area with which I am most closely concerned, the agriculture unit, has recruited outstanding producers from each of the last three categories in recent years.) Inasmuch as the inclusion of the civil service was intended to relate to the supposed security of employment in the BBC it certainly no longer applies if, indeed, it ever did. Two producers of agricultural programmes have been cast out during my time for failing to achieve the high standard expected of them. The corporation is no sinecure—not in the production area at any rate. By and large a producer is as good as his last programme; it is a highly competitive field with too many thrusting, talented people jostling for too few programme slots. If one falls by the wayside there is always another ready to fill the gap. And the Corporation does not necessarily have to fire its production staff to get rid of them. It can simply remove the outlet for their work. No creative person is likely to be happy for long without a vehicle for his energies and he soon takes the hint and finds a job elsewhere.

I was extraordinarily lucky to join the Corporation at a turning point in its existence. I was to experience the tail end of the old Reithian era and the beginning of the new order, epitomised by the recently-appointed Director General, Hugh Carleton Greene, a man who, according to one of the Sunday papers of the time, 'preferred pubs to clubs'. The BBC of those days was, I suppose, a trifle stuffy, staffed at the top end by trusty, well-meaning men and women, some of whom had worked with the great man himself.

Symptomatic of the times, though unimportant in itself, was the occasion on which a Regional Controller, demi-gods when I joined the staff, was visiting an out-station to hold annual interviews, the occasions on which each member of the staff has his annual report (an assessment of his year's work and conduct by his superior) read to him. The Controller on this occasion was staying the night with a senior producer, an old friend who had been on his staff for many years. The following morning, driving back to the BBC centre, the producer suddenly realised that he was due to have his annual interview that day and was not wearing a suit. Should he, he enquired of the Controller sitting in the passenger seat beside him, go back and change? The Controller considered the situation for a few seconds and concluded that perhaps he ought. So they solemnly turned the car round and drove ten miles back to allow the producer to be properly turned out for the great occasion.

It was also a significant period in practical terms when I joined the BBC because I came in on the portable tape recorder explosion. They had, of course, been using quarter-inch tape for

PLATES 16 AND 17.
Above, our host for the first and the 100th *On Your Farm* breakfast programmes, Peter Smith, among the ablest farmers of his generation. His family farms in five different counties; the helicopter enables him to drop in on them.

Right, although dubbed the 'TV Vet', Eddie Straiton cut his broadcasting teeth in radio and has enlivened many an *On Your Farm* programme. This kiss-of-life picture is appropriate in view of his abiding interest in bovine obstetrics.

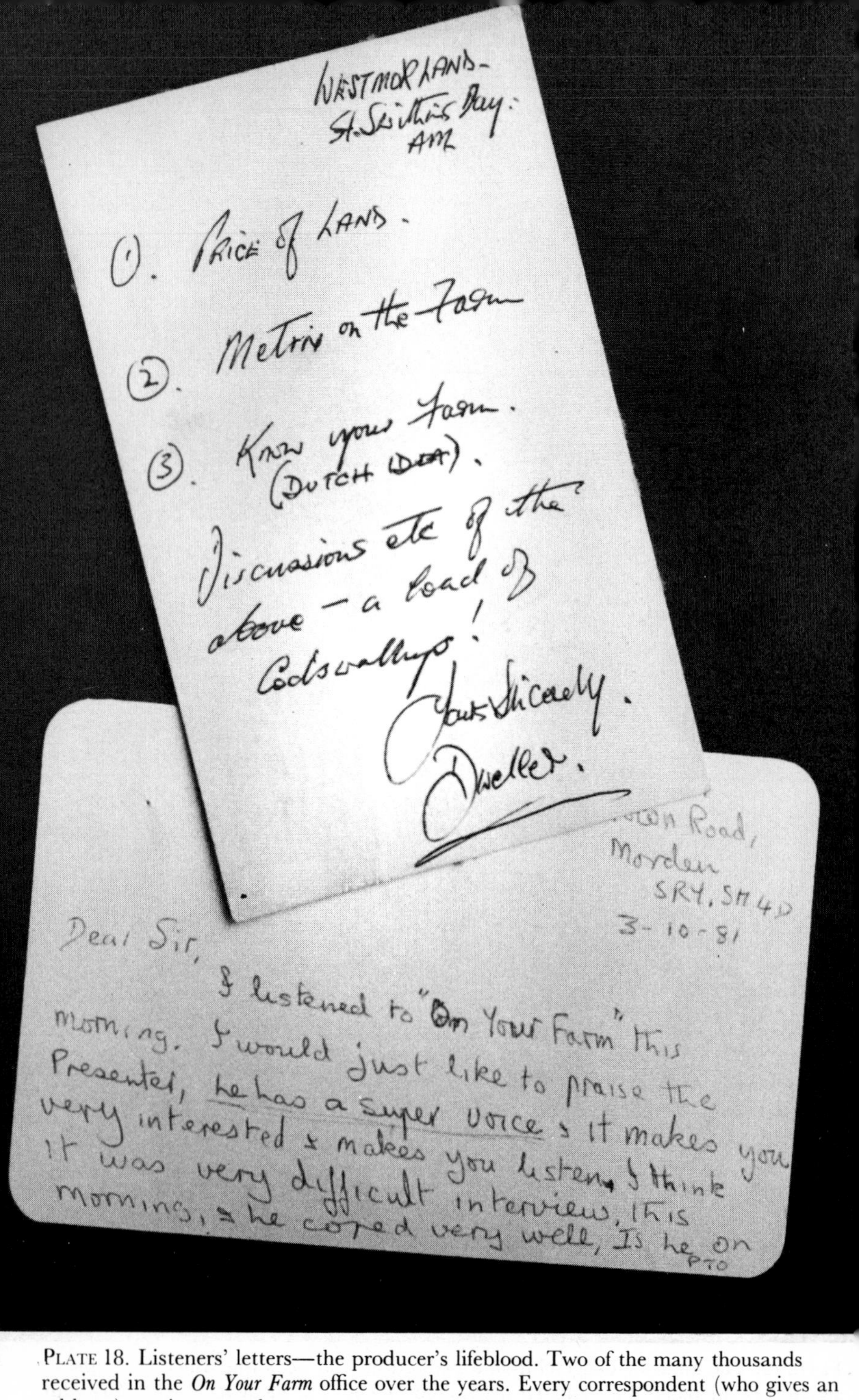

WESTMORLAND -
St. Swithin's Day:
AM

(1). Price of Land.

(2). Metric on the Farm

(3). Know your Farm.
(DUTCH [illegible]).

Discussions etc of the above — a load of Codswallop!

Yours Sincerely.
Dweller.

[illegible] Road,
Morden
SRY. SM4 [illegible]
3-10-81

Dear Sir,

I listened to "On Your Farm" this morning. I would just like to praise the Presenter, he has a super voice & it makes you very interested & makes you listen. I think it was very difficult interview, this morning, & he coped very well. Is he on

PTO

PLATE 18. Listeners' letters—the producer's lifeblood. Two of the many thousands received in the *On Your Farm* office over the years. Every correspondent (who gives an address) receives a reply.

Dear Mr . Chairman of "Down on your farm"
I feel I must write, though I wish you no harm
For much as your programme is liked by us all
The signature tune is beginning to pall.
For week after week we find this never varies
Implying we're no more than dimwitted fairies-
Or at best, country yokels with straws in our hair
An image so many townsfolk like to share.
In Industrial Britain, we farmers excel
So come, you experts who in Birmingham dwell
Just give us a tune that behoves and bestirs
Introducing this programme which weekly occurs;
Like "The Yeomen of England" or maybe for that matter
Haydyn's "Creation" or"We plough fields and scatter"
The choice is so wide and our cause so deserving
So please pick one, our social position preserving.
For the Archers and Grundys and that crummy crowd
A trite country dance tune might well be allowed
But for Farmers in REAL life, come, we can do better,
And that I suggest is the gist of my letter.
(Forbid it I say , my dear Anthony Parkin
That your name be changed overnight into Larkin)

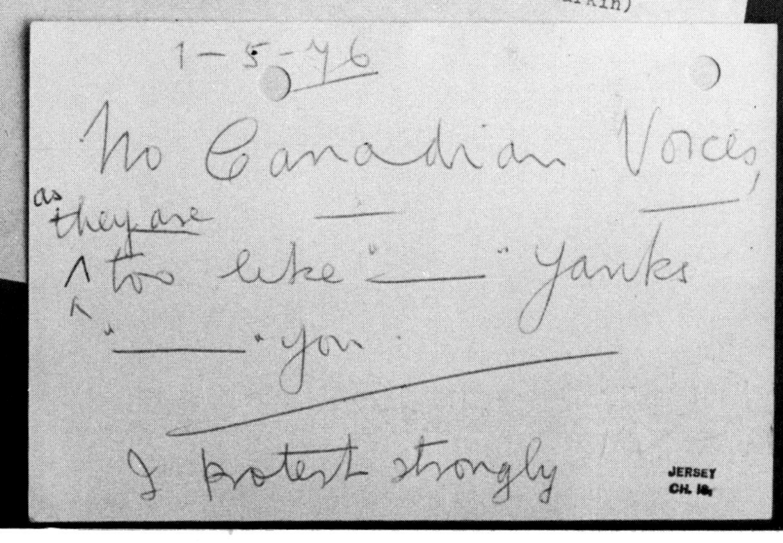
1 – 5 – 76

No Canadian Voices,
as they are
too like " — " Yanks
" — " you

I protest strongly

JERSEY
CH. I8.

PLATE 19. The amusing doggerel from a Bedfordshire farmer's wife which led to the signature tune poll of 1981 and our decision to stick to 'The Ploughboy'—together with a typical outburst from our friend in Jersey.

PLATES 20 AND 21. *Left*, the BBC's network agricultural team with (third from left) Jock Gallagher, Head of Network Radio at Birmingham where the unit is centred. Martin Small (left) and Allan Wright produce our early morning *Farming Today* and also take a turn at producing *On Your Farm*.

Below, the broadcasting staff of the Fiji Ministry of Agriculture with whom I spent two months in 1979. I do not know how much I taught them but I certainly learned a lot.

Plates 22 and 23. Two well-known personalities who have had close connection with *On Your Farm* and its predecessor.

Left, Ted Moult who presented *A Living From the Land* for twelve months and who has contributed earthy comments on numerous occasions to its successor.

Below, Phil Drabble who played a part in many of our live outside broadcasts, where his professionalism often saved the day.

PLATES 24 AND 25. *Above*, Stuart Seaton, editor of *Farmers' Guardian*, at work on a script for *On Your Farm*. He was one of the original interviewers on the breakfast editions and has made frequent contributions to the programme over the years.

Below, 'testing, testing.' Ken Ford tries out his tape recorder before using it on behalf of *On Your Farm* which he sometimes produces. Based in Leeds, he is the popular producer/presenter of *Gardeners' Question Time*.

PLATES 26 AND 27. *Above*, Dan Slater, a regular and valued contributor to *On Your Farm*, notably in the horticultural field, on his farm in Worcestershire. He retired to devote his time to painting but re-emerges occasionally to take part in the programme.

Below, Peter Williams, whose shrewd interpretation and analysis of agricultural politics and practice have enhanced the *On Your Farm* programme from time to time at his home in Swaledale.

PLATE 28. At home foddering the cattle with Wendy and Sue. (Of the rest of the family Ian is a land agent, married, in Durham; Sarah is married to a naval officer and lives in Hampshire, and Anna works in Fleet Street.)

some time but were still cutting the last of the wax discs for the Birmingham news room in Broad Street when I appeared on the scene. I never actually recorded on to disc although I can remember the machines on the back seat of the big black Humber when the BBC turned up for an important agricultural event which I happened to be reporting in the fifties. The change to tape, with its ease of editing, opened up completely new horizons for producers and I was fortunate to come in on that phase and not to have had my attitude to programme-making restricted by the old system with all its limitations.

Being Director General of the BBC must rank as one of the most onerous jobs in the country. I have already referred to the public scrutiny to which every producer's work is exposed and the strain which this brings in its train. A DG is trouble-shooter for hundreds of producers and no programme from *Thought for the Day* to *Tom and Jerry* is free of critics. Add to that the multiplicity of other responsibilities including the essential one of securing adequate funding, and the knighthood when it comes must seem thoroughly well-earned.

In the light of this it is hard to argue that the DG on whose coat tails I entered the establishment in 1960 exercised his powers wisely. In some ways the swinging sixties were an unfortunate decade for the BBC, aiding and abetting as it did the decline in public morals and also paving the way for 'Broadcasting in the Seventies'. Change was obviously overdue but it seemed to me at the time that Greene as housekeeper of the BBC was imprudent to the point of irresponsibility in his freedom with the keys. Some closets needing unlocking, perhaps, even the odd room here and there but not the whole mansion. It needed opening up carefully and selectively. He appeared to unbuckle his housekeeper's belt, remove the keys and hand over the whole bunch with an invitation to the eager producers who grabbed them to get on with it and see what happened. He could argue, no doubt, that he had commercial television breathing down his neck but it looked as if he just failed to appreciate the immense influence of the BBC on the public at that time—for good or ill.

It was all rollicking fun – *That Was The Week That Was* and so on – but was it the kind of leadership one was justified in expecting at the helm of the nation's media flagship? As a radio producer at the time I had tremendous difficulty in trying to reconcile the standards rigorously upheld in the early sixties at our regular programme board, where the month's output from Birmingham was critically discussed, with what I saw on my own television screen at home. Greene could not have stemmed the flood single-handed but he seriously under-estimated the power of the BBC and the result of the example he allowed it to set on the rest of the media. It was Shula Archer and the pill writ large.

It was not long before there were few institutions and activities which had not been subjected to analysis, dissection and destructive mockery by the various organs of the media. This led to the publication of a letter in *The Times* in 1967 from the then Archdeacon of Auckland referring to a suggestion that talks over the air be given by 'eminent personalities' in an attempt to stem the rot. Under the heading 'Trahison des Clercs' he wrote:

> I wonder what they can appeal to. The continued sniping at all our loyalties, which has been a feature of almost every means of mass communication for the past few years, has left the bulk of the people puzzled and depressed and in a mood of increasing cynicism about everything. There is nothing particularly intelligent or enlightened about this continual carping, though those who do it seem to think that there is. With nothing left that he feels certain about, except the need to safeguard his own interests and the conviction that he is the best judge of what they are, the ordinary man is convinced that he should fight for his own hand. The permissive society in which we live reinforces this by assuring him that he need defer little, if at all, to the opinion of others. So freedom has degenerated into individualism, which is next door to anarchy.
>
> The danger inherent in this is twofold. Either we shall collapse entirely or normal people, sick of the confusion and frustration, will begin to look around for some authoritative system to impose from above the discipline we seem unable to impose on ourselves. We need above all a fresh faith in the basic loyalties by which we can live and a renewed sense of duty.
>
> The intelligentsia have betrayed us . . .

That was in 1967 and the situation has developed further since then with the result that there is not much left for my children to cleave to. Religion, politics, education, authority of all kinds and sex have all had the pernicious treatment, being picked over and ridiculed. If one drama producer allowed d---, a second had to permit b------ and a third was not satisfied until he had included f--- in a play. Let it all hang out, they say. What for? Is it to impress colleagues because there seems little evidence that the great British public welcomes the trend. I am lucky to have spent my time with Auntie in areas where it has been more rewarding to try and build bridges than drive wedges and where the worst anyone can come out with in a programme is 'artificial insemination'. But to be serious we have seen the pulling down of much that was valuable in our society and it is difficult to see how it can be replaced. Shibboleths needed challenging no doubt and the media had an essential role to play but the whole thing has gone over the top and we have reached the stage where every icon has its iconoclast waiting with pen, microphone or camera.

While all this was going on in the sixties the ground was being prepared for a drastic change in the structure of radio. Under the BBC's plan 'Broadcasting in the Seventies' the Regions, by which the Corporation had hitherto always set such great store, were to be abolished and local radio introduced. The theory seemed to be that because the Regions were badly defined they no longer had any significance—no one seemed to have considered re-drawing their boundaries along the lines which took community of interest into account rather than out-dated transmitter coverage. Because local radio worked so well in the United States, it was argued, it ought to go well here—although the States would be the last place on earth I would look to for a model in broadcasting of any kind. Cynics say that when British Rail wants to close a line it causes trains to run at inconvenient times and then points to the fact that no one uses them. I would not claim that this was going on in the BBC Regions during the sixties but there was certainly no apparent move to strengthen the Regions at a time when one might have thought it desirable. The writing, in the closed circles at the top at any rate, appeared to be on the wall. I was one of the producers who put their necks on the chopping block by signing a letter to *The Times* in 1970 protesting at the proposed changes. We could, under the terms of our contracts, have been sacked for this but I suspect that there were too many of us to fire. Instead I received a friendly, explanatory letter from my Controller (not the one who insisted on suits for annual interviews) warning me not to do it again. In reply I wrote as follows:

> Nobody likes rocking the boat, least of all me. I signed the letter because to be silent is to appear to agree with the changes which are being made. I object basically to what must amount to the substitution of quantity for quality in broadcasting. I feel that the Regions should have been re-planned and strengthened rather than that the resources should be dissipated over the wider field of local radio. I believe that the apparent miracle of producing more on virtually the same money will be done at the expense of two things, quality and staff.

Amusingly, in retrospect, the very day on which 'the letter' appeared in *The Times* my wife and I had been invited to one of those *Archers* parties I referred to earlier which must have been to celebrate twenty years of the programme and at which the then Director General, Charles Curran, was chief guest. In spite of every effort to maintain a low profile I found myself being hauled off to be introduced and for one awful moment thought he was going to reach into his inside pocket and produce a list of offending producers saying ominously 'Parkin, did you say?' But his attention was on other things and I began to enjoy the party rather more after that.

Two thoughts come to mind in the light of events since. One is that the more recently set-up or envisaged local radio stations are beginning to approach in size and community of interest the re-planned regions some of us had in mind in the sixties. The other is that in spite of all the furore – or perhaps because of it – Radio 4 has emerged as what must be the finest service of its kind in the world with the result that the producers who signed *The Times* letters in 1970 and their successors were leaping to its defence when it was threatened ten years later. Long may it continue. In my limited experience of life nearly all change seems to be for the worse. The trouble is that there are too many people – often, ironically in the BBC's case, fearful of media criticism – who feel that *not* to change is weakness.

It would no doubt be construed as grossly naïve to suggest that most of our troubles stem from the introduction of commercial television back in the fifties which paved the way naturally for commercial radio in the seventies. It was inevitable—or so we are told. It had to come. What could you do to stop it? In my experience it is possible to prevent almost anything before it starts. What is virtually impossible is to stop anything once it has started. Thus a government could never successfully ban smoking or alcohol, but it can stop marijuana, or at least refuse to legalise it. There is a garage I pass every day which has one of the most dangerous exits on to an A road which it is possible to imagine. No authority would give permission for it nowadays but equally it is beyond the ability of anyone to prevent its continued use. The demand for commercial television and commercial radio came from a well-organised lobby consisting of people who were going to benefit from it. A responsible government, with its eyes beyond the next election (or was it perhaps paying debts incurred at the last one?) should have foreseen the long-term effect of a decision to hand the most compelling of the media over to the moneymakers. The government propaganda machine is incredibly powerful when it swings into action. Can anyone really argue that a government which persuaded this country into joining the EEC was incapable of using the same means to persuade voters that it really was not in their long-term interest to allow the proliferation of radio and television which has taken place? The BBC would almost certainly not have embarked on local radio if it had not seen commercial radio on the horizon. And now it is breakfast television.

I cannot help reacting to attacks on the BBC immoderately and gave up going to the pub with the best beer in the neighbourhood because of the landlord's repeated snide remarks. So when someone of apparent standing questioned in a letter to the press whether the BBC was any longer necessary and argued that it offered nothing which commercial television did not provide except the absence of advertisements I had to respond. Not through the press – that would have needed permission and approval of a reply – but direct. I was astonished to find that someone who claimed to have sat on two government committees of enquiry (not on broadcasting) could not see that our commercial television, which is probably the finest commercial television in the world, is only as good as it is *because* of the existence of the BBC. When he replied to my comparisons with American television programmes by saying that he found them at least as good as anything the BBC had produced I realised there was no point in arguing. His main point was that the cost of the BBC was unnecessary, the assumption being that commercial television was free. Where does he think the money comes from to pay for the programmes and the staff, most of whom earn considerably more than their opposite numbers in the BBC? The income of the commercial television and radio companies is considerably higher than that of the BBC and it all comes from advertising. My wife helps to pay for it every time she buys a packet of soap powder.

Still, like cable television, this proliferation of radio and television output creates jobs, and who dares argue in these days of high unemployment with anything which does that? After all we are taking in Japan's nuclear washing for the same reason. Is there no more constructive solution to unemployment? It is surprising that no one has suggested a chain of state-owned brothels? There is a labour intensive industry for you. Think of all the madams, all the chuckers-out and all the ash-tray emptiers apart from the central figures. Is any remedy with long term social risks to be encouraged so long as it creates jobs?

The propagation of television channels which the onset of cable heralds was condemned in a BBC phone-in programme by, of all people, a young American television scriptwriter. He referred to the social damage which he thought the multiplication of channels had already inflicted in the United States – the 'plug-in drug' as he called it – and told the audience that when television 'reached the level of running water' it cheapened everything on it from Shakespeare to *Sale of the Century*. 'You'll be sorry,' was his final warning. I am sure we shall.

Meanwhile there is a dangerous myth abroad which needs

challenging, the myth that every time you open up a new radio or television channel you expand or extend choice. It has become a parrot cry in some quarters, the need to 'expand choice' for the viewer or listener. In practice, every time you make another channel available it could be argued that you actually restrict choice. You would only expand it if our ability to take it all in were expanded and probably not even then. But since we have only one pair of ears and one pair of eyes and are capable of absorbing only one programme at a time, to increase the number of radio channels from say three to four actually reduces our chance of hearing any particular programme from one in three to one in four. As there is only a limited amount of raw material to go at (even news) and a limited amount of money available, the chances are that the material which used to go into three channels will be spread across four. So the listener has a slenderer chance of hearing an attenuated service.

My argument made unsuccessfully at numerous talk-ins on the future of radio is that we would do the listening public a good turn if we actually reduced the number of channels and, using our professional skill, distilled into these the programmes which radio does well. As it is, in many urban areas now there are six radio channels to choose from. It could be argued that there are at least nine daily newspapers available but this is a false analogy inasmuch as you could, if so inclined, buy all the newspapers and read all of them which is not possible with six radio programmes being transmitted simultaneously.

In case it may be thought that I am speaking from the security of an established weekly programme let me say that no programme is in an unassailable position, but I was once asked if I would like forty-five minutes for *On Your Farm* instead of the thirty it occupied and I said 'No, thanks.' A colleague said: 'You must be mad—you should have taken it and asked for an assistant.' But who would it have benefited? Half an hour in my opinion is plenty long enough to expect to hold people at that time of day. To increase the duration by fifty per cent would have laid us open to two dangers. We might have developed into an 'agricultural *Today*', in other words a programme the listener is expected to opt in and out of. Secondly there might have been weeks when there was not enough to fill three-quarters of an hour properly and we would be left simply spreading what should have been thirty minutes' material over forty-five. I may have been wrong but, tempting though the offer was, my considered view was that the audience would not have been better off in the long run.

Another myth which needs exploding is that a disaster every hour on the hour is good for us. There seems to be a feeling that if something is possible it is therefore desirable; if we can get a report from an obscure Turkish village about a gas cylinder exploding at a private party killing a large number of guests that in itself makes it newsworthy. This particular news item came hot on the heels of a serious Italian earthquake and simply served to blunt the edge of compassion. I cannot see why the nerves of the listeners need to have been further shattered by news of what seemed to be a totally irrelevant tragedy in Turkey. Or a jail riot in America, filling our screens with needless violence. What for? Because we could get film? Because it was a thin day for news? The effect is simply a further dulling of the senses as the capacity to absorb disaster and violence is sated. The trouble is that the great news monster has been created and must somehow be satisfied.

It is questionable too, whether the pressuring of politicians, captains of industry, trade union leaders and the like for the instant answer to the situation which obviously demands careful consideration is in the public interest—and surely it is to serve the public that the media exist. Sometimes they must be forced in order to provide a response to make the wrong one and are then stuck with it and feel they must reinforce it. Because they will not be allowed to forget it. 'But yesterday, Minister, you said . . .' And not to have an answer is construed as weakness when it should often be interpreted as the contrary, as a determination to give the matter the necessary thought. Let us hope that the media are not too close to the action when people start thinking of pressing nuclear buttons. 'But yesterday, Mr President, you said . . .'

Earlier I likened the BBC to a mistress and ever since I seem to have been complaining about her. To have an affair with someone does not necessarily mean that you agree with her in every respect but basically what I have been deprecating is the proliferation of the media in general during the last twenty-odd years. It is a very personal view, both as an employee of the BBC and a consumer of the product, and one which would not necessarily be shared by all of my radio colleagues at Pebble Mill. Agriculture is in a special position inasmuch as the centre of our network output in both radio and television is Birmingham. When 'Broadcasting in the Seventies' was implemented I was already producing the weekly network programme *On Your Farm* so that, as a producer, the changes had little effect whereas some of my colleagues in drama, music, sport and religion who had exercised a very large degree of autonomy under the old regional system found themselves acting more as agents for London. So once again I was lucky.

Meanwhile, the reputation of the BBC abroad seems as high as ever. Travelling round the world on an agricultural ticket over the last couple of decades I have been amazed at the effect of those three magic letters – BBC – in opening doors. I can only recall two occasions on which it failed to work. Once was in Madrid during the days of Franco. I was attending a big agricultural fair and was told that all I need do to get in was to say I was from the BBC. There was a long queue at the gate so I walked to the head of it where two policemen, bristling with small arms stood. One walked a step or two to meet me. 'BBC,' I said, using the appropriate pronunciation, showing him my identification card. My Spanish was not quite up to his reply but I think the gist of it, accompanied by appropriate threatening gestures, was 'I don't care a damn who you are, get back in the queue along with everyone else.'

The other occasion was during the DC10 groundings a few years ago. I was holed up in Los Angeles with no plane, no luggage and only a handful of dollars which I used on a cab to take me to a hotel. It was about eleven o'clock at night and the scenario from which I had temporarily escaped at the airport might well have been written by Franz Kafka. So it was with some relief that I tumbled out at an attractive-looking hotel to be greeted in the foyer with the effusive voice of the cheerful desk clerk:

'Good evening sir. And for you a king-size bed. If you'll just complete the details,' and he placed the form carefully in front of me. I filled it in and he scrutinised it.

'And how will you be paying, sir?' The tone was still genial.

'Well,' I said, 'I've plenty of travellers' cheques.'

His eyes narrowed fractionally. 'Travellers' cheques,' he said doubtfully. 'May I see the travellers' cheques please?'

I pushed them over. They were the ones issued by my bank.

'No sir. I'm afraid I can't accept these. What about your credit card?'

'Look,' I showed him. 'It says "valid anywhere in the world".'

'Not here, sir. Your credit card,' he insisted.

'I'm afraid I haven't got a credit card.'

His eyes narrowed to slits. 'You have no credit card,' he said disbelievingly. Clearly anyone without a credit card had no business to be in his hotel. Or indeed at large, at all. I tried my passport with no effect. He turned it round a couple of times and handed it back without a word. A man with no credit card. Wait until I tell the wife, he seemed to be saying. Then I played my trump card. My BBC identity card complete with picture. That should get me a bed and credit until I could visit the bank I could see across the road in the morning.

'Surely you've heard of the BBC,' I said.

He removed the form and put it under the desk. 'Can't say I have,' he replied. And that was that. Of course it would have been different on the east coast I told myself as I walked the quarter-mile to another hotel where they cashed the travellers' cheques at an appalling discount and provided an expensive bed.

A couple of thousand miles further north, over the border in Saskatchewan, it was altogether different. I was there making a programme at the same time as a writers' get-together was being held. One of the sessions was on writing for radio. Would I care to look in on the seminar? I was ushered into a room with perhaps thirty people, being addressed informally by one who turned out to be the chairperson. My guide went up and muttered something in his ear. He stopped talking, his whole appearance took on a more responsible air and he spoke gravely but smoothly.

'Ladies and gentlemen, I understand that we have just been joined by a gentleman from the BBC. Would you care to come up here, sir?' I walked somewhat abashed to the front of the room, conscious of having interrupted their discussion.

'I wonder whether you would care to let us have your views, Mr Parker,' the chairman said, deferentially.

'My views?' I exclaimed. 'What on?'

'Well—anything' came the reply.

ELEVEN

Interviews and Other Diversions

When my youngest daughter was even younger she was a faithful listener to *On Your Farm*. Now, at the age of fifteen she is more likely to switch on Radio 1 if indeed she is awake at that time on a Saturday morning. But I remember her coming into our bedroom when she was about six or seven, having heard the programme, and saying: 'Daddy, I don't think you know much about farming. You keep having to ask other people questions about it.'

While there was doubtless some truth in her observation she may also have been lodging an unconscious early protest at the over-use, as some people see it, of the interview as a way of putting things over on radio. Personally, I do not feel that the well-structured interview needs defending but since it has been alleged that we resort to it too often I am quite happy to come to its rescue, at least in so far as I may have been guilty of abusing it.

To appreciate the role of the interview in modern broadcasting you have to look not at its disadvantages but at its advantages and at the alternatives. To begin with it is a very natural form of communication. You want to know something, someone else has the answers, so you ask him a string of questions. What could be more sensible? A skilful interviewer tries to put himself in the position of the listener and to anticipate his queries. Obviously he does not always manage this and there are plenty of frustrated people at the loudspeaker end of the chain thinking, 'why on earth doesn't the idiot ask him this or that?' But the really big advantage of the interview is that it can be accomplished with minimal effort and expenditure of time on the part of the interviewee. The indisputable fact is that at least half the interviews which have been broadcast in *On Your Farm* over the years would never have been recorded in the first place had it not been for the ability of an interviewer with a Uher (portable tape recorder) to grab someone at a conference or demonstration and assure them that 'it will only take five minutes.' Most of the people whose views we want in our programmes are working under enormous pressure. What the interview does is to make it an easy and relatively painless process for them to put these views over leaving the interviewer, the professional, to do the preparatory and often subsequent work. I will come back to the interviewer's role in a moment but let us first look at the alternatives.

One of them is the discussion, a format of which we make a lot of use in *On Your Farm*. Indeed one of the really rewarding aspects of a producer's work is to be able to bring together in front of a microphone people who would never otherwise have met and perhaps to bring out points which would not otherwise have been made. When it comes off it is marvellous but there are many obstacles to be overcome before the final ten-minute package, or whatever was allocated, matures. Let us suppose, for example, that a conservationist who works in Somerset has made a controversial speech over the weekend which I feel ought to be reflected in next Saturday's programme. I happen to know that there is a farmer in Cumbria who holds a diametrically opposite point of view and it would be interesting to get the two together. But because the polarisation of viewpoints can lead to a sterile discussion, what about including that academic from Wye College who has no axe to grind, sits on one or two key committees and always talks sense?

The question now is, how do we get them together, assuming that they are all willing to participate? One thing is almost certain—they are very unlikely to agree to come to Pebble Mill which would be the most satisfactory solution. For both the farmer and the academic it would mean a complete day away from their other work. The conservationist may be persuaded to drive up the M5 and we could get the other two in more local studios linked to Pebble Mill. Hopes of an easy answer are dashed on telephoning the conservationist only to learn that he is away all day at a conference. He will be back in the office tomorrow. My difficulty is that I am tied up with *The Archers* on Tuesday and Wednesday so that any recording will have to be fixed for Thursday or Friday. And while my secretary can pursue people by telephone, I have to talk to them when she has got hold of them and explain what I have in mind. So we find where the conservationist's conference is taking place and see if we can get him to a telephone during the coffee or lunch break. A quick call to the farmer establishes that he is busy drilling and will not be back until half past one. Let us try the academic. He is lecturing, it turns out, but should be back in his office at twelve. We leave a message at the hotel where the conference is being held asking the conservationist to telephone us and hope he gets it. Then there is nothing more we can do until midday. Meanwhile we are left wondering whether this particular part of the programme will mature, or not.

At five past twelve my secretary tries the academic but he has not returned. By twenty past he has looked in briefly but dashed off again saying he will be back at 2.15. Has he anything in his diary for Thursday or Friday? Looks pretty full, says his secretary protectively. Meanwhile the conservationist has not rung so we telephone the hotel again to make sure he has got the message. I see that it is going to be another day with a cheese roll in the office for me. At half past one I ring the farmer but he has not come in for lunch. The drill has broken down and he has dashed into town for a spare. Try again in an hour's time. Then the telephone rings. It is the conservationist. Yes, he could manage Thursday or Friday and does not mind coming to Pebble Mill. Things are beginning to look up. We make contact with the academic soon after two and he is quite willing to take part in the discussion which I outline. He cannot manage Thursday but is in London for a meeting on Friday and could manage between eleven and one o'clock. When we eventually contact the farmer, nearer three than half past two, he is understandably short-tempered. They have had two breakdowns with the drill and the weather forecast is unfavourable. He is far more concerned with getting his barley in than in taking part in a radio discussion and anyway he is sitting on the bench on Friday morning. I try a

Yorkshire farmer who, I know, has strong views on the subject. He has not yet returned from market, although he is usually back by now, says his wife. Could we try again in half an hour, perhaps?

On the assumption that I can persuade him to take part we then begin phase two of the operation—booking the necessary studios and connecting lines between Broadcasting House in London and Pebble Mill and between BBC Leeds and us, for an hour between eleven and one on Friday. Settle for half an hour if the worst comes to the worst, I tell my secretary. This takes some time to clear and in the meantime I contact the Yorkshire farmer and persuade him to come to Leeds, assuming the studio is available. He agrees somewhat reluctantly as he should be at an NFU executive meeting. Then we hear that there are no studios available on Friday morning in London between eleven and one. Back to the academic to see whether he could possibly make it earlier or later. He is out of the office by now and not expected back. . . .

I will not go on but this is certainly no exaggeration of the difficulty involved in arranging a simple ten-minute discussion. In fact I frequently leave the office at half past six on a Monday evening having achieved virtually nothing. Neither am I complaining; it is, after all, what I am paid for. I am just trying to explain why a situation like this eventually could resolve itself into yet another interview—on this occasion with the conservationist who was prepared to come to Birmingham.

What other alternatives have we? The scripted talk—what is wrong with that? It ought to be an opportunity to put over a carefully thought out viewpoint, logically and with no interruption from that infernal interviewer. Well, there are several things wrong with it, unfortunately. For one thing writing a good radio script is a highly skilled job; and putting it over – 'lifting it off the page' as we call it so that it does not sound as if it is being read – is another. It also takes a long time to write a script and travel to a studio to record it, and the end product from the unprofessional contributor tends to stick out like a sore thumb in an informal programme like *On Your Farm*. There is no way that most of the people we haul in at short notice for an interview could be persuaded to go home, write a script, come to Pebble Mill and spend an hour or two recording it. And even if they were capable and willing, they would understandably tell us what they wanted us to hear which may well not be what the listener wanted to know.

Some people have the gift of 'ad libbing' from a few headings on the back of an envelope, arguing a point logically and cogently with one eye on the clock. Hew Watt, the well-known Essex farmer is one; Ted Owen who farmed until recently in Somerset, another. Monty Keen, editor of *British Farmer and Stockbreeder*, a third. There are others, but it is a rare skill. On three occasions over the twenty years of producing *On Your Farm* I have tried to introduce a feature in which an individual would be encouraged to let his or her hair down on a subject of their own choice without the help of an interviewer—'What I say' was the first; 'Platform' was the second attempt and the most recent was called 'Fieldspace'. None of them lasted longer than a year. The reason? The sheer difficulty of accomplishing the apparently simple task of recording them in broadcastable form. There was no difficulty finding volunteers, no shortage of subject matter. But it was exceedingly hard to make it work. Either they would ad lib for ten minutes when we had agreed on three or they would have scripted something which sounded very contrived and exactly what I did not want. Or, and this frequently happened, they would have had second thoughts in between agreeing to do the piece and actually recording it and tender an extremely adulterated version of what I had heard them say over a glass of beer or what they had promised to deliver over the telephone. We achieved some really excellent pieces in all three series but also some pretty mediocre ones. Often it would end up with my having to interview them in an attempt to get them to deliver the agreed goods and then edit out the questions to make it appear to be an ad-libbed piece. Which, I suppose, is one way of getting rid of the interview although not always to my mind an entirely honest one.

Gone are the spacious days, I am afraid, when producing a short radio talk was the occasion for lunch and a bottle of Beaujolais followed by a couple of visits to the studio. Malcolm Muggeridge mentions in his diaries going to the BBC to 'practise my broadcast'. A scripted talk, presumably; even the interviews were scripted in those days. But then, to be fair, most broadcasting was done live, and the interviews were recorded on wax discs like gramophone records which were extremely hard to edit. The interviews actually contained what had been said during the run through. But it was an edited version which was read, often not very convincingly.

So it looks as if the interview is here to stay and providing that the interviewer has done his homework and behaves courteously I cannot see much wrong with it. The question is how much prep should he do. I do not believe in preparing the actual questions in advance which applies a straitjacket over the whole interview; but only on the very rarest occasion would I embark upon an interview without a fair idea of how it was going to start, how it was going to develop and how it was going to wind up. On most occasions it is an insult to the interviewee and to the listener to start unprepared. The computer folk have a saying which could well be adopted by interviewers: 'Garbage in garbage out.' In other words you cannot expect a good interview if you have not thought the thing out in advance.

There are the exceptions which prove the rule, of course. Once at a meeting of the UN Food and Agriculture Organisation in Rome I heard the then US Secretary of Agriculture make a speech which was so provocative that I felt I must get an interview with him and put a few 'ifs' and 'buts'. I hurried off before the end of the session to see his aides and was told there was absolutely no chance as he was flying to Chicago immediately the session was over. It was one of those occasions when the magic three letters 'BBC' failed to work. Ah well, you cannot win them all I thought and went back to a report I had been writing. Five minutes later there was a hand on my shoulder: 'Mr Freeman says you can interview him in the car on the way to the airport,' said one of his team. I grabbed my tape recorder and rushed off, and as we sat in the back of the huge limousine I recorded without a note the interview of a lifetime. When I returned the word had got round and the world's press wanted to know what he had said. Would I agree to a playback? A room was hastily requisitioned by the FAO radio staff and soon it was crammed to the doors with journalists from half the countries of the world. The famous tape was put on, the button pressed—and nothing happened. In my excitement I had forgotten to switch the recorder on.

That disconcerting experience serves to illustrate just how much there is for a one-man interviewing team, which is what many of us are most of the time, to keep an eye on. Not only do you have to plan your interview, try to ask the right questions and listen to the answers and keep an eye on the stop-watch but you also have to make sure that you are holding the mike in the right position for both of you, that the background noise is not too high (or too low if background is essential), that you have tested the recorder beforehand, got a fresh tape on, batteries well charged—and that it is switched on with the little red needle peaking to the right point. It may be easy for the interviewee but it is far from straightforward for the interviewer.

The first interview I ever did was only a few days after I had joined the BBC. I went to talk to a farmer who had just changed over from milk churns to a bulk tank. He met me in the yard, looking rather embarrassed with his hand half over his mouth. It turned out that he had sneezed violently while in the smallest room that morning just as he pulled the chain and had the horrific experience of seeing his false teeth disappear round the bend. The result was a somewhat gummy interview and I began to think I might have been better off staying as a journalist.

Since then I have done some thousands of interviews and have met with some pretty weird experiences, but the unexpected is the norm in that job. After all, it may be my 2,749th interview but for the interviewee it is quite likely to be the first. Although I have not gone in for the deliberately unusual – diving bells or airships – I must have recorded interviews in most of the possible (and near-impossible) situations. Castles, crofts, buses, planes, cars, boats and dozens of others as well as every conceivable part of a farm. One of the oddest locations for an interview was the ladies' powder room in the old Red Horse Hotel in Stratford-upon-Avon (now a branch of Marks and Spencer) which a kind manager offered me during a meeting at the hotel, promising to stand guard outside.

Among the most curious of my interviews took place on a farm not far from Lisbon when I was doing a programme on British emigrants of whom there were quite a few in the late sixties. The farmer's wife, whom I was to interview, was holding a very young baby while we chatted about the subject matter of the recording. She made no attempt to put it in its cot which was nearby. I fiddled with my notes while waiting for her to settle it. Eventually I said: 'Right then, when you're ready,' to which she replied, 'Whenever you like.' Further self-conscious shuffling on my part took place as I pretended to check the microphone and so on when, to my astonishment, she lifted her shirt and started to feed the baby. 'OK,' she said, 'go ahead.' And that is how we did the interview—with a slight pause halfway through as she changed sides. And a very good piece it turned out to be.

Michael Clark and I were preparing to interview the winner of the cheese championship at the old Dairy Show at Olympia when he appeared suddenly to be threatened with some grave affliction. We had chatted to him about the interview, told him how long we wanted, taken a bit of level and then, in answer to Mike's first question, his rich West Country voice deserted him and all he could conjure up were some choking noises from halfway down his throat. Mike and I watched mesmerised as he tried to get out the words. At last by a mixture of lip reading and careful listening we found that what he was trying to get out sotto voce were the words 'Duke and Duchess.' We turned round to find ourselves face to face with the Duke and Duchess of Kent who were touring the Show and had been brought along to meet the cheese champion who had of course seen the whole procession arrive and then come to a halt behind us. Their Royal Highnesses seemed quite unperturbed but there were signs of acute agitation among the retinue—so we withdrew and returned later.

I do not know whether we in this country take our liberty too much for granted. We probably enjoy as a nation greater freedom than any other country in the world. It was brought home to me one day when David Richardson and I were covering the Paris Show—the international agricultural fair held at the Porte de Versailles each February. Over a drink in the fantastic food and wine hall, we got talking to a French farmer who from a BBC producer's viewpoint started off with a tremendous advantage. He spoke fluent English. But as the chat proceeded we found he not only was easy to listen to, he had some very provocative things to say about French farming and particularly about the way in which, to his mind, co-operation was being forced on French farmers by government policy. Since *our* government was at that time holding up the growth of the co-operative movement in France as an example to be followed by British farmers this was obviously extremely interesting, especially as our French friend was a leading figure in agricultural circles and a Count to boot.

I have been too long in the game to expect people to repeat what they say in a bar in front of a microphone but thought I would chance my luck anyway. How about giving us an interview, I asked him. At first he refused, but refused for a reason which I cannot conceive ever entering the head of a farmer this side of the channel. If he did, he said, the French Ministry of Agriculture would make life difficult for him in some way. He exported cattle and they might find it impossible to give him a permit, or they might withhold a grant. I told him that we could use the interview anonymously and, after some persuasion he agreed, as it was a subject he obviously felt strongly about. As anyone who has been to the Salon in March will know, the background noise is pretty deafening and this was too important a subject to be spoiled with excessive background. I left David talking to M. le Comte while I went off to see whether ORTF (the French radio and television service—which also, incidentally, enjoys considerably less freedom than the BBC) could lend us a studio for a quarter of an hour or so.

Summoning up my best French I asked the only chap around, a little sour-faced man wearing a tartan beret with a button on top. He gave me the impression – through a succession of grunts and shrugs – that he had been instructed to co-operate with the BBC if approached but that given his own way he would have shown me the door.

'En quinze minutes?' I asked.

He drew on his Gauloises, lifted his eyes to heaven and said 'Oui.'

I went back half-expecting that it was all off but David had done his stuff and the Count was still willing. What followed was pure farce. I had not realised that ORTF had only one studio in its large complex at the Salon and that was a huge semi-circular affair, thirty or forty feet across. The whole of the curved wall was made entirely of glass, the idea being to allow the visitors to see a studio at work. It was into this studio that we were unexpectedly thrust—David, me and the Frenchman who wanted to remain anonymous. It was like being in a giant floodlit goldfish bowl and half Paris had their noses pressed to the glass. The Count took one look and then, being a man of action, went over to the long curtains and gave them a vicious tug. The curtains, malheureusement, were for purely decorative purposes with only a yard of cloth at each side to cover perhaps fifty feet of glass. The curtain came down, the rail came down and various other flimsy bits of the temporary studio cascaded onto the floor. The door opened and in came the incredulous studio manager with his tartan beret and the inevitable Gauloises. My French was not quite up to what he said as he surveyed the ruins of his beautiful studio but I got the impression that it would be a long time before he helped the BBC again. There were two high stools round a mike slung from the ceiling. The Frenchman sat with his back to the crowd and his coat collar turned up—and gave David a surprisingly good interview, in the circumstances.

For the last fifteen years or so we have broadcast under the *On Your Farm* banner an occasional series with the subtitle 'Taking the Pulse'. The idea has been to go to a county or occasionally an area which cuts across county boundaries but which shares a common farming interest and 'take the pulse' of its agriculture. We spend a maximum of a couple of days in the area and make no claim at all to producing a definitive programme on its agriculture. What we try to do is to project a picture of the county as we see it that week—it may be covered in snow or suffering from drought; it may be busy with silage making or with corn harvest; it may be a period of agricultural buoyancy or of depression. It is a sort of farming *Down Your*

Way but covering a wider geographical area and, I would like to think, with a bit more bite in the questions. But we try to find the same interesting cross-section of interviewees although we do not usually have the musical interludes.

When I say 'we' I should explain that I usually work in tandem with a freelance interviewer on these occasions, normally a broadcasting farmer such as David Richardson, Michael Clark or David Butler. The idea is that whoever I am working with does the interviews and I subsequently introduce and link the pieces, although sometimes I cannot resist the temptation to join the interviews. But it is very much a team job and we bounce ideas off each other as we drive around the area and plan the next interview. The essence of this series is surprise. Until we get to the county we have little idea whom we shall be talking to—and they have no idea at all. Of course we do a fair bit of homework and usually kick off with a rundown on the area from someone with a good knowledge of its agriculture and the changes which are taking place. A chat to the ADAS (Ministry's Agricultural Development and Advisory Service) people and the NFU office puts us on the track of some interesting *possible* interviewees. I stress possible because there is no way of knowing at that stage whether they will be at home when we call or willing to talk to us if they are. Sometimes to avoid an unnecessary detour we will telephone half an hour or so in advance to find out if the unsuspecting interviewee is available—sometimes we simply drive into the yard and get out of the car with the tape recorder running, always being careful of course to tell them what it is for.

People are amazingly co-operative on these occasions and seem to enter into the spirit of the exercise. And if the farmer is not at home—well, we have had some excellent interviews with wives and workers. Not that we stick to farmers—we try to cover the whole agricultural spectrum including vets and agricultural merchants, bank managers and auctioneers, machinery dealers and inseminators, contractors and MFHs as well as farm workers, landowners and farmers: anyone who plays a part in making the agricultural clock tick. If, as we drive along, we see someone harrowing or the tanker driver collecting someone's milk or a gang riddling potatoes, we will stop and try and get something on tape.

It can be a nail-biting experience as one interview after another fails to materialise. The first chap is not in, the second does not want to be interviewed, the third is willing but not fluent enough, the fourth attempt just does not get anywhere. All the time the seconds are ticking by. The programme has been trailed the previous Saturday and here we are with the best part of a day gone and nothing to show for it. It was on one of these occasions that David Richardson and I were driving down a quiet road in Leicestershire, with things looking pretty bleak, when we came upon a chap leading a large flock of ewes.

'Come on, David,' I said, 'you can interview him as we slide past this lot.'

I got the tape recorder ready and fed the mike across to David who was driving. We drew alongside the man who seemed not the slightest bit surprised at having a microphone poked at him from a passing car.

'We're doing some interviews for the BBC *On Your Farm* programme. Would you like to say a word or two?' urged David.

To which he replied: 'Pliss? No speak English. Me from Czechoslovakia.' Trust us, towards the end of an unproductive day, to find the only non-English-speaking shepherd in the whole country.

In a situation like that of course it would have been impossible to give the interview any preparation. It would have to be totally spontaneous although we had obviously thought ourselves into the Leicestershire scene and so would not have been starting entirely from scratch. It was like that on another occasion when David Butler and I were 'taking the pulse' of farming in Berkshire. It was a miserable day in January, a moderate blizzard was blowing, hardly the sort of day to find folk working in the fields. And then, through the falling snow we picked out a man muck spreading, not sitting on a tractor with the dung spinning out behind him, but spreading heaps of farm yard manure with a fork. It was too good an opportunity to miss. No point in frightening him though, so I suggested that David went over on his own. David Butler was the sort of chap who could get a reasonable interview out of a stone. Well, not quite, perhaps, but he could make an interview with monosyllabic answers stand up he was so fluent. David disappeared into the thickening snow-storm, Uher slung over his shoulder, and emerged five minutes later saying that he had recorded quite a nice interview.

'What did he say?' I asked.

'He kept saying "Keeps I warm" to every question I put to him.'

'Was he surprised to see you?'

'Yes,' said David. 'He asked if there had been an aircraft crash as I approached out of the snow, but I assured him that it was only the BBC.'

On this occasion, for some reason, we enjoyed the unusual luxury of a secretary so I asked her to go and get his name and address, just for the records. She returned, covered in snow, soon afterwards, obviously enjoying a quiet laugh.

'I told him I was from the BBC,' she related, and he said, 'Well, I'm jiggered. You're the second person I've had from the BBC this morning!'

I could fill the rest of this book with stories arising out of this series. There was the man in Kirkudbrightshire who drew a knife on us. He was an itinerant slaughterer who went from farm to farm killing and dressing a lamb or a pig for domestic consumption. In reply to David Richardson's opening gambit he produced one of the ugliest knives I have ever seen and then, pulling up his shirt sleeve, began to shave the hairs off his arm to demonstrate its sharpness. David paled and went right off mike when he offered to do the same for him. There was Mrs Ossie Johnson, the Northumberland farmer's wife, likening the 400-year old bastle house in the farm yard with its four-foot-thick walls to her husband:

> When you get to know hill farmers and see how resilient they are you begin to look at the buildings and think what they've descended from. The whole Border history has matured these sort of people. My husband copes with a lot of crises – for

> instance when the weather's very bad – but he never gets flustered, he just gets on with them. And when you look at these buildings you know these farmers have something akin to them—the stone and their characters. And looking at this bastle house—it's really like my husband's character.

That took place in one of several programmes of this kind which I have done with Peter Williams, a brilliant, warm, lovely man who would have made a highly successful barrister but who has chosen instead to live life his way, with his delightful wife and family, a life which included a meteoric career in agricultural education and fifteen years farming in the Lake District. Peter is a genius at finding interesting people to interview but on one occasion when we found ourselves in a somewhat embarrassing situation it was a result of a purely chance encounter with an old acquaintance of Peter's. We were 'taking the pulse' of farming across the Pennines from Sedbergh in Cumbria to Richmond in Yorkshire. On these occasions I often tried to visit a market and we had looked in at Hawes which has the distinction of being the highest livestock market in England.

We had recorded some of the selling of local store cattle and a fascinating piece about Swaledale sheep. Then as we were leaving the mart Peter bumped into an old friend of his, Laurie Rukin, who used to be a member of the Keld Singers, a group of farmers from the Yorkshire Dales who got together to please themselves and other people and who had broadcast many years ago for the BBC. We were chatting away in the main road at Hawes with the lorries thundering by when I suddenly had a bright idea. Why not ask this farmer for a song about the area? To my surprise, although he was turned seventy and no longer in his singing prime, he readily agreed. He knew two suitable songs, he told me, one of fourteen verses and one of four. Taking all things into consideration I quickly settled for the latter—but where to record? You had to shout to make yourself heard over the traffic where we were.

Nothing daunted, Mr. Rukin led us into someone's back garden and there, sheltered from the noise, he launched into a lovely song about 'Beautiful Dale, home of the Swale'. By the end of the first verse and chorus I could sense Peter's Welsh blood rising. The second chorus saw him joining in tentatively. By the third chorus he was harmonising perfectly. And that was when the owner of the house appeared on the scene. The look of sheer incredulity on her face at the sight of two men in her garden singing at the tops of their voices and a third holding a microphone between them is something I shall never forget. I held up my hand and she remained quiet until the fourth verse was on the tape. Then came explanations, apologies and forgiveness.

People seem to be far less inhibited by the sight of a microphone than one might expect. Perhaps the familiar sight of so many of them waving about on television has bred a certain contempt although it was many moons ago that I was recording an interview with a farmer deep in one of his orchards when his foreman hove into sight a hundred yards away. He made a beeline for us but I felt sure that the sight of a microphone would slow him up. Not a bit. He walked straight up to my interviewee who was in full flow and said, ' 'Scuse me interrupting boss but we've finished those boxes. Do you want us to carry on pruning?'

On another occasion the postman insisted on delivering the letters right into the hand of the chap I was in the middle of interviewing and I once completed a recording, which had started in the quiet of an empty hotel dining room, with three waiters noisily laying up the tables, including the one we were sitting at. That was one of many instances where it had been a case of act quickly or lose the interview altogether. A conference was taking place, the man I wanted to interview had to hurry off (it is always the more interesting speakers who have to leave early) and so I had found the first quiet place to take him to record. In this case – and in many others – it started quietly enough and ended in near chaos. I remember once, without permission, taking an interviewee into a vacant office only to be disturbed a minute or two later by its owner who turned out to be a Very Important Person indeed. Charm and a thick skin are needed in this job. I am frequently amazed at the situations into which distinguished people allow themselves to be persuaded for purposes of an interview. The

Bishop of London (when Bishop of Truro) allowed me to take him behind the heavy window curtains of the Café Royal to cut out the background noise, following a conference on rural areas.

Background noise is present to some degree in almost every interview recorded outside a studio. It is impossible to avoid it these days – birds sing, traffic hums, aeroplanes roar – and it can be used effectively to enhance an interview. The unmistakable noise of the milking machine, the roar of the forage harvester, the gabble of the auctioneer, the squealing of pigs can all be used to establish location. The trouble is you do not always want them at the same level throughout the interview. I usually get over this situation by saying something like 'Bit noisy in here, let's wander outside,' and continue to record with a more acceptable level.

A question I am quite likely to be asked when we are editing a tape is 'Got any atmos?' What the tape editor means is did I record some of the background atmosphere, apart from what is under the speech? This can be invaluable in achieving a smooth entry and exit from the interview. Recording 'atmosphere' is one of those things which is easy to forget in the heat of the moment and one's attempts are often frustrated by people talking over it anyway.

Perhaps this is a good point for me to pay tribute to the gallant folk who week after week, month after month, work with me in studios and editing channels turning the raw material into finished programmes. I am referring to the members of our Audio Unit, the unsung heroes of many a good programme. Although well versed in the technical secrets of radio many of them also have a high aesthetic appreciation and enthusiasm to match. To work with one of these talented people on a programme and to see him or her getting the same kick out of achieving a high-quality end-product is one of the real delights of the job. They have usually not shared in the fun of gathering the material and they will not be publicly associated with its transmission by way of a credit. Many of them are producers manqué but it is one of the sad facts of life that few of them will have the opportunity to produce their own programmes, only because the pyramid gets smaller the nearer the top. Meanwhile I readily admit that *On Your Farm* is frequently 'made' in the editing channel.

But why do we need to 'edit' tapes? I am sometimes asked by those who feel the word has a sinister connotation. In my experience there are two reasons for editing. One is the simple operation of getting a quart into a pint pot. If there are five minutes available for an interview and the interviewee insists on talking for eight, then three minutes have to be edited out. The second reason is purely to make the interview easier to understand. That can involve removing anything from the noise of a lorry going by which drowns speech to a question and answer which just do not get us anywhere, from tidying up circumlocution while retaining the sense to cutting awkward gaps when either party has dried up. Editing a tape is not something one embarks on lightly. It is approached in a highly responsible way by both the producer who decides where to cut and the tape editor who actually wields the razor (and quite often suggests a better place to insert it) and demands fairness and honesty. To those who suspect that it is used actually to distort the sense of what someone is trying to say I can put my hand on my heart and tell them that in nearly twenty-five years as a producer I have never even heard the idea mentioned let alone being practised. Of course, every time you make a cut to reduce the length you run the risk of removing something which someone wanted to be broadcast. But if you only have thirty minutes and they have talked for forty, what can you do? All I can say is that I have never had a complaint. Most comments are to the contrary varying from 'My goodness, you did a good job on that tape' to the slightly more naïve, 'sounded much better than I thought it would.'

The trouble is that now people have got so used to the idea that all tapes are edited that it induces a laxness. 'You can cut that bit out' or 'Of course, you'll tidy it up.' I remember a Cabinet Minister saying in the middle of what could easily have been a *live* interview (inasmuch as it was being recorded for another programme and in another country) 'No, you can edit all that stuff out, can't you' and then start his answer again. One man who must have wished for a bit of editing I met some years back after a demonstration had been held on his farm. I could not make the event but had agreed to call in during the evening on my way home from another job, to interview him. He was hopping mad when he greeted me. Commercial television had interviewed him that day for a regional magazine programme and he had just watched it go out. Apparently a plane had gone over during the interview and they had stopped after that question and answer and recorded it again. Unfortunately, they had failed to edit out one of the identical questions and that was what was making him so cross. I did not realise the full measure of his discomfort however until a week or two later when I met the chap who had done the interview, an old chum of mine. I told him how angry his interviewee had been at having both questions left in.

'Ah,' he said, 'but what he didn't tell you was that he gave a totally different *answer* the second time.'

In spite of all the editing we still occasionally leave things in which, in retrospect, I wish I had taken out. I have a habit of waking up between the hours of about 2.30 a.m. and 5.30 a.m. and worrying gently about things in general—not an uncomfortable time normally but just as motoring crystallises one's thoughts (which is why I always carry a pocket tape recorder in the car) so lying in bed in the wee small hours tends to distort them. I have a facility, born of years and years of mucking about with other people's words, for remembering interviews, scripts, linking material almost word for word. On this particular Saturday morning I fell to worrying about the words I had used to introduce a Continental cattle dealer I had interviewed. I had described him as a swashbuckling character, I recalled as I lay in bed. I knew he would be listening to the programme and I knew that he was one of the sharpest operators in the business. The adjective had come readily to mind the previous day, but might it be taken amiss by him? Could he argue that it held him up to contempt and ridicule or any of the other things which a slander is supposed to do? Eventually, at the risk of waking my wife, I had to go down and look in the dictionary. The first one I consulted gave me little comfort, the second even less and the third volume made me feel that perhaps I should not have said it. It was about four o'clock by now. Not much I could do about it for the time being but I ought to get the offending word removed. He was the sort of chap who might just take it amiss and decide to sue in which case some of the definitions in my dictionaries would not look too good.

I sweated until about half past five and then rang Broadcasting House in London, got myself put through to a helpful engineer and explained my predicament. I was able to tell him from the programme script more or less where he would find it on the tape and it seemed to me that we could get rid of 'swashbuckling' without upsetting the sense of the link. I had introduced the interview with the words 'Recently I met a swashbuckling Dutchman who . . .' He told me that he would find the tape and cut the word. I asked him if he would ring me back and confirm that he had accomplished the deed and he replied rather tersely: 'I've told you that I'll do it. There's no need for me to ring back.' When someone is doing you a favour at half past five on a Saturday morning you do not argue, so I left it at that. By quarter past six, the suspense was too much so I telephoned again just to reassure myself, only to be met with an entirely new voice.

'I don't know anything about it, mate,' it said. 'I've only just come on.' And presumably my saviour had just gone off.

I sweated for another hour or so until the programme went out—without any reference to swashbuckling. It was one of those silly situations born of waking and worrying at four o'clock in the morning. Is that not the time when they interrogate prisoners, when their resistance is at its lowest ebb? In the clear light of day I should have been extremely unlikely to have done anything about it—and neither, I feel sure, would the Dutchman.

TWELVE

Personal Perspective

A mixture of heredity and environment dictates the kind of people we are and I have been singularly fortunate in the way that both have smoothed my passage through the agricultural media; to be able to feel equally at home with peers and ploughmen, to have sown and reaped the same field through all the vicissitudes of the season, to have lost a valuable beast and yet know what it is like to pay for the weekend joint. What is learned before one is ten is not easily cast aside. My parents, both from humble backgrounds, gave me two pieces of advice which have stood me in good stead ever since. My father's constant admonition was that we are put in this world primarily to work and that success is the result of five per cent inspiration and ninety-five per cent perspiration. My mother's perpetual warning was against snobbery in any of its forms. She was fond of quoting Robert Burns on the subject and 'when Adam delved and Eve span, who was then the gentleman?' This was not the product of a lowly upbringing: it went with her through life and later on she was equally at home occupying a privileged seat at some state occasion—or doing the ironing.

Although my father left school at the age of fourteen he was, according to his contemporaries, already marked out for greatness. Less than four years later he was in the trenches where he spent the next three and a half years until a bad wound brought him back to hospital in this country. After the war he began in the industry which was to occupy him for the whole of his working life—the docks. To relate that where Ernest Bevin had been organising the dockers in Bristol my father was secretary to the Port of Bristol Employers' Association perhaps puts things in the wrong perspective. Bevin was certainly left wing but my father was far from being to the right. He used to like to tell the story of a meeting of the employers' association in the twenties at which one shipowner said 'Gentlemen, I think our Secretary's a bloody Socialist.'

He shared many things with Bevin including friendship and mutual respect. Both came from West Country rural stock—my father's forbears as far back as we have traced them, into the eighteenth century, were all agricultural labourers near Barnstaple. Both were scandalised by the way in which dockers were treated: the way in which they had to line up like animals at six o'clock every morning, some to be selected for work and the rest to be sent home empty-handed. One of the first things which Bevin did on becoming Minister of Labour in 1940 was to send for my father and ask him to start the National Dock Labour Corporation, later to become the National Dock Labour Board, the organisation set up to employ all the dockers in the country. Thus was their joint ambition, the de-casualisation of dockers, achieved and my father found himself boss of a business employing eighty thousand men in the days when it was possible to 'boss' without everyone coming out on strike.

He was to live to see things move too far in the other direction, perhaps, with some dockers getting paid enormous sums of money for doing very little. It is in the nature of pendulums to swing. He died, listening to *The Archers*, at the age of 75 not long after celebrating fifty years of happy marriage, with the First World War's shrapnel still working its way out of his body. He was described in an obituary in *The Times* as 'a really great industrial arbitrator . . . Though he was the least didactic and opinionated of men, he always gave the impression of being right.'

The trouble was that he was so wrapped up in his work, especially during the 1939–45 war, that he had little time for his four children and allowed them to tumble in and out of education and careers with little if any guidance. Which explains perhaps how I come to be doing what I am doing. I remember only one attempt at trying to coax me into a career. I was about seventeen and without any fixed plans although I was already working on a farm. He came home one Saturday afternoon after a good lunch and announced that I was to become a quantity surveyor. His lunchtime companion had assured him that there would be an enormous demand for them with all the post-war building and rebuilding. He thrust a copy of a magazine called *The Quantity Surveyor* at me and glared. 'Well, what do you say?' I said that it was not a job I had ever thought about at which he turned on his heel and strode out of the room shouting. 'Right, that's the last time I try to help you with a career.' It was also the first time and the whole session had lasted about two minutes. I think, on reflection, that I have had more fun as a BBC producer than I would have had as a quantity surveyor.

I was born, almost in a cab, on the way to a nursing home in Clifton, Bristol, in the year of the General Strike. Shortly afterwards we moved to a modest house with a large garden on the outskirts of the city in a suburban village with two working blacksmiths' shops busy shoeing horses from dawn until dusk. Perhaps it was leaning over the half-doors of these establishments (until we were chased away); perhaps it was wandering through the fields at the back of the house where fringe farming still existed; perhaps it was our caravan holidays on farms—usually the only caravan on the place; perhaps it was watching things grow in the garden which gave me my interest in farming, or perhaps it was heredity after missing a generation. I cannot be sure, but every step I took thereafter moved me inexorably nearer to it.

Trying to get back to his roots my father bought a cottage in North Devon long before second homes became fashionable and in those spacious, carefree (for me) pre-war days we would spend as much time there as possible, launched into a totally new social and physical environment. It was a close-knit area of small mainly livestock-rearing farms and we were very much the foreigners but I was enthralled with it all. When the war started my father decided to evacuate the family there – that included my mother, younger brother and sister – which meant taking me away from my boarding school and sending me to the local secondary school, a five-mile bus ride away. I did not complain. When the expected bombs failed to fall we all moved back to Bristol again and I went back to boarding school. But only for a term or so. By the summer of 1940 we were back in Devon with my father commuting at weekends.

It was about this time that I realised that we were not all one big happy family—that there were the 'haves' and 'have-nots'. During the term at the secondary school, which I had thoroughly enjoyed, incidentally, because it was less demanding, I had been working with a boy called Newton on making an incubator out of a large biscuit tin. We had lined it carefully with old blanket, fixed a shelf all round the inside for the eggs and an electric light bulb to supply the heat. I was disappointed not to return to the school as we had not had a chance to try it out. Imagine my surprise, the following summer, to see Newton busy slashing the hedges near our cottage, with an older man.

'What on earth are you doing?' I exclaimed.

'Working,' he replied.

I couldn't understand it. 'Working?' I asked. 'Who for?'

'The Council,' came the cheery answer.

The fact was, of course, that Newton, whom I had regarded as being in every way an equal at school, had reached the magic age of fourteen and had been cast out to find a job. The local council was as good an employer as any other, and as I walked home I did not know whether to feel sorry for him or envy him.

When it became clear from the way the war was going that we were in for a long stay, my mother decided that life in a cottage with no water, lavatory, electricity, gas or telephone was more than she wanted to cope with on her own and so we rented half a large farmhouse a few miles out of Barnstaple and I was sent to the local grammar school. This was yet another step along the agricultural path because the farm on which we lived was a busy mixed holding with a small milking herd, beef cattle, a flock of sheep, poultry galore and growing dredge corn and swedes for the stock. I too had reached the age of fourteen and if Newton could work, well so could I. There is a saying that one boy is worth a man; two boys are worth half a boy and three boys are a damned nuisance. I was the only boy on the place and within a year or so there were not many jobs I had not had a go at, including ploughing with a team of horses. The second summer I was there I worked from dawn until dusk, first with the hay, then with the corn harvest. All for no payment—the excitement and fulfilment of doing a useful job and being part of a team were reward enough, not to mention those wonderful harvest teas brought out to the fields in cloth-covered baskets. Then one day, at the end of harvest, the farmer took me on one side and said he would like to show his appreciation. He felt in his waistcoat pocket and produced a shilling. 'There you are, boy,' he said magnanimously. 'You just keep going on like that.' Later that day I showed the coin to my sister. It slipped out of my hand and fell into a deep stone water trough from which I never did recover it.

It was the same farmer who at a war-time charity dance in Barnstaple offered a brace of rabbits as a prize. As he was not known for his generosity eyebrows were raised in astonishment until the lucky man came to claim his prize. 'There's plenty of rabbits on my farm,' he was told. 'Best come up and shoot a couple.' He certainly had an abundance of them. I once saw four fall to a single cartridge.

By this time my father was busy in London and wanted his family to join him—not in the blitzed capital, of course, but twenty-odd miles out on the North Downs. He rented a small Georgian manor house on the Chevening estate of Lord Stanhope and, when we reached it complete with the hens and rabbits we had collected, I was delighted to find that it had two and a half acres of land and some stables. Having taken School Certificate and done reasonably well I decided that I had had enough of school.

I started to clear the overgrown land including scything an acre of paddock for hay and looked round for some stock. My meagre resources at that time, I found when I reached Sevenoaks market, could only run to a goat. I bought her for £3 and then had to consider how to get her home. The train went to within two miles of our house. I took her – or rather she took me – over to the railway station where the chap in the parcels office unwisely insisted on weighing her. I warned him but he insisted and received several hundred pellets all over his office for his pains.

The train journey was uneventful but the final couple of miles was taken at a gallop. Nothing done by that goat, or by any of those we subsequently had, in any way endeared me to the species and I soon switched to cattle. There was a limit to how many cattle, even young ones, I could keep on the acre or so which was not down to garden, orchard or tennis lawns so it was not long before I was off in search of more land. I secured the tenancy of about fifteen acres adjoining ours and went into unofficial partnership with my father. He supplied the capital, I did the work and we split the profit fifty-fifty.

Meanwhile I had taken a job on the Home Farm at Chevening and had three years there on the basic wage and learning all the time. I spent a year as under carter working with a pair of Shires, a year as second cowman with a herd of Dairy Shorthorns, still my favourite breed, I had a spell as shepherd's boy with a flock of Romney Marsh ewes and a longish stint in the estate office learning how a 3,000-acre estate is run. I had no idea at the time where it was all leading; it was enough that I was doing it.

It was hard work. I was up at five if I was milking, half past five if working with the horses otherwise I could have a lie in until six. It was a mile across the fields and through the woods to the farm—downhill in the morning when I was fresh and a climb up the North Downs at night when I was tired. At hay and harvest time we would be at it until nine o'clock. Then, being a normal healthy lad, courting had to be fitted in and often, having climbed to our 700-foot eyrie, it would only be to eat a quick meal and off down the hill again on my push bike towards Sevenoaks and a girl friend. Back at midnight or later.

But superimposed on this, to me, idyllic existence were two other situations entirely new to my experience. The first was a dramatic change in social status associated with occupation of one of the minor 'big houses'. With the passage of years it seems trite but at the time, to a sixteen-year-old, brought up on the outskirts of Bristol or in a cottage in Devon, it was confusing to say the least to find myself referred to by the locals as 'the young Master' and addressed as 'Mister Tony'. At the same time I was busy all day forking muck or hoeing mangolds. I expect the locals wondered why I was working on a farm but put it down to 'the war' which was changing the world as they had known it.

On top of this was the strange relationship which developed

between the owner of the estate, Lord Stanhope, and me. James, 7th Earl Stanhope, KG, PC, DSO, MC, had had a distinguished military and political career, including many years at the Admiralty, Foreign Office and Board of Education and had been leader of the House of Lords from 1938 until 1940. His occupation when I made his acquaintance was 'peer, landowner and farmer', a description with which I became familiar through filling in so many forms on his behalf during my spell in the estate office. Chevening was and still is a remarkable house, one of our great stately homes, designed by Inigo Jones. It achieved some fame after Lord Stanhope's death in 1967 because of the possibility of its becoming the home of the Prince of Wales. In 1980 the Prince decided not to make use of it – I can only assume because the hunting was not up to Gloucestershire standards – and since then it has been used by the Foreign Secretary to entertain official visitors. When I started working at Chevening Lord Stanhope was in his early sixties, his wife had died two years earlier and he had no children. He was no longer politically involved and I think he was lonely. It is the only explanation I can think of for his attitude towards this young stranger living in one of his houses, working on his farm and trying desperately to shed his carefully cultivated Devon dialect. I not infrequently ate with him à deux at Chevening, much to the barely-concealed disgust of his butler, and I shot with him while the rest of the time I was milking his cows and stooking his sheaves.

I would set off for a day's partridge shooting with him – there were plenty of partridge in those days – and at lunchtime a car would materialise, rugs would be laid out, hampers unpacked, bottles opened before the butler retired to a discreet distance while his Lordship and I ate an al fresco lunch. When the pheasant season began we usually went back to the house for lunch. The company on those occasions was mixed, often including well-known public figures of the day. I remember one particular week because on Friday I spent the day on one of the most menial tasks I have ever performed – shovelling ash and clinker from the back yard at Chevening House to fill some potholes in the farm road – while the following day saw me at lunch passing the sloe gin to General (later Lord)

Ismay, Military Secretary to the War Cabinet and one of Churchill's right-hand men, who was shooting that day. The conversation, unbelievably with the benefit of hindsight, was whether party politics would ever return. Having hardly become politically aware, needless to say I was content to listen and carry on passing – and sampling – the decanters.

It was an old-fashioned self-contained estate. Lord Stanhope owned everything and was the benevolent dictator over numerous employees and tenants. The whole village belonged to him plus various lodges, keepers' and farm workers' cottages as well as a number of tenanted farms. He generated his own electricity and employed a plumber, bricklayer, gardeners, a chauffeur and handymen of various sorts although, because it was wartime, there was a degree of doubling up. One could sense just the rumbling of social revolution, urged on by the war. The foreman of the threshing gang, for example, always insisted on addressing him as Mr Stanhope and giving him the worst job when he volunteered, as he invariably did, to help. Clearing the cavings was the task reserved for his Lordship who ended the session smothered in dust and with eyebrows bigger than Denis Healey's. And then there was the story, still told in hushed tones and with a quick look round to make sure no one could overhear, about the man (no longer in the area) who had been told by his Lordship to open a gate to allow him through on his horse. On refusing he was alleged to have been challenged with the words: 'Do you know who I am? I'm Lord Stanhope,' to which he was alleged to have answered: 'I don't care whether you're Lord Jesus Christ, get down and open the ——— gate yourself.' Knowing Stanhope and his gentle, courteous manner I am certain that the story was apocryphal but its very repetition was a sign of the social changes which were on the way.

I often have a friendly argument with my son regarding the value of our respective practical farming experience. He can claim to have worked on dozens of farms in various countries round the world. But I do not think that in a single instance he ever stayed long enough to see the crop he drilled harvested, or the land he harvested re-sown. Not, I hasten to add, because he was put going but because he was so keen to 'broaden' his experience. Apart from the Devon farm where I worked as a schoolboy, I had experience on only one. That was the 420-acre Home Farm at Chevening where I worked for three and half dung-haulings, as the saying goes, since I returned there for six months or so after leaving the RAF. To plough, harrow, drill and hoe a field and then to harvest the crop, not once but thrice; to work alongside the same team of chaps for three seasons; to see a calf born, reared, served, have her first calf and then to milk her is of more lasting benefit I would argue than sowing on a farm in one country and reaping on a farm in another, or putting the ram to the ewes on one farm, lambing on another twelve thousand miles away and shearing on a third. It is a moot point but those years left an indelible impression and taught me the meaning of hard work.

Both the resident agent and the foreman were Scots who vied with each other to extract the most from the work-force. Of course in those days there were no fore-end loaders to take the backache out of muck carting; every cubic yard had to be forked on to horse-drawn carts, hauled to the field, pulled off in heaps and spread by hand. There were no combine harvesters – at least in our area – and every field had to be cut with a binder and the sheaves stooked, forked on to wagons, forked off again on to ricks which were thatched and later opened up and threshed and the straw built into further stacks. There were no balers – at least on that farm – and the hay was all swept to the rick to be cut out with a hayknife during the winter. No weedkillers, pre- or post-emergence, had been developed, no monogerm seed or precision drills, and every acre of mangolds or beans had to be hoed meticulously by horse and hand. Every 2¼ cwt. bag of wheat had to be carried up the granary steps on our backs. When I returned to the farm after the war I remember stepping forward to the wagon to take a sack of wheat and crumpling under the weight of it. Three years on His Majesty's service had softened me up. Yet I do not remember many complaints. Perhaps we were all swept along on a tide of patriotic fervour, feeding a besieged nation at war and all that sort of thing.

We were expected to work in all weathers (no tractor cabs, in fact no tractor until I had been there for some time) and I remember that on one particular day when we were supposed to be lifting mangolds we sheltered from the rain in a shed. It was no ordinary rain: when it fell into puddles it splashed back up three inches. It was not long before the foreman made his appearance. There were four of us there—Percy, two land girls and myself. He sent Percy out with a curt jerk of his head. To the land girls he said 'Come on girls, get on with it. Bit of rain won't hurt you.' Then he turned and gave me a withering, contemptuous look and said, his heavy Scots accent putting even more feeling into the words: 'As for you—I thought you were educated.'

Only once did I object to doing a job. A septic tank at one of the cottages in the village had seized up solid and a team including me was despatched to dig it out. I protested that this hardly qualified as farm work and was sent off on my own to make thatching spars. I wish, in retrospect, that I had taken my turn with the others rather than pointing up the difference.

But difference there undoubtedly was, much as I wished, as would most lads of seventeen, to conform. Lord Stanhope continued to treat me almost as an adopted son, one day summoning me to the house to see his Garter robes which he was to wear at Windsor at the annual gathering of Knights. I stood alone in the huge hall at Chevening as he walked slowly down the spectacular staircase and then proceeded to explain to me the significance of the various articles of his apparel. Because one of his forbears had subscribed to the building of the Albert Hall, Stanhope was entitled to two of the best seats for everything which took place there in perpetuity. I was given carte blanche with these tickets and since the Queen's Hall had been destroyed by one of Hitler's bombs the Albert Hall was the centre of London's musical concerts and I made full use of them. Had I been a different sort of person I suppose I could have capitalised on the situation and gone back after university to help run the estate or perhaps rent a farm. As it was the relationship dwindled after I left to join up. It blossomed for a short time on my return but by then I was being beckoned by Fleet Street and marriage, and although we corresponded off and on until his death, I did not return to Chevening.

At the same time that I was leading my 'double life' there and being 'the young master' at home I was also being sucked into my father's new life in London, a life which involved a flat in Mayfair with a resident couple to look after him and all the trappings of power. It was by no means unusual for me to spend the day walking behind a horse and harrow and the evening at the Players' Theatre or dining at the Piccadilly Grill. It was a lot for a simple lad to digest. From 1943 onwards I was living on borrowed time so far as my work on the farm was concerned. I had volunteered for the RAF when I was 17¼ and was selected for training as PNB (pilot, navigator or bomber) and placed on 'deferred service'. The air force was reluctant to indulge in the expensive training of too many pilots and I was one of a reserve to be called on as the occasion demanded. Fortunately we did not lose as many aircrew as had been anticipated with the result that, after two more re-selection boards, I was not called up until 1945, long after my eighteenth birthday. Although I was able to wear the silver badge of the RAFVR it was ironic that the reward for volunteering long before most of my age group was to be called up long afterwards and I must confess to being impatient with those who assumed that it was because I was working on a farm. However, had I started my pilot training in 1943 I might not now be here to tell the tale.

There were two other people who had a profound impact on my life. One was F. G. Thomas, the gifted university lecturer who was seconded to help my father start the National Dock Labour Corporation—and stayed until he retired. It was he who persuaded me how essential it was that I should go to university; I would have been unlikely to have gone but for his perseverance and encouragement. To do so meant spending most of my free time during two RAF years in India, when my chums were swimming, drinking or lying in the sun, doing a protracted correspondence course in order to matriculate. I say protracted advisedly since each essay sent to my tutors in London took at least six weeks in the post.

The other great influence was Don Lamble, art editor for many years on *The Farmers Weekly* and still one of my closest friends. When I joined the paper at the age of twenty-two it was he who filled in some of the many gaps in my knowledge – particularly in politics and the arts – left by a disrupted wartime education and inadequate parental guidance.

One aspect of my working life which I commend, although it happened fortuitously, was starting in London. Ten years in Fleet Street have made the twenty-odd years which have followed in the provinces an enjoyable and enriching experience. So often people spend too long eating their hearts out in the provinces wishing they were in London and then being disappointed if and when they get there. To gain the experience of the metropolis first and then transport it to the provinces seems a more satisfactory situation all round but for various reasons is not often possible. Once again I was very lucky.

I was not so fortunate, in my job, in my parents' choice of names. Anthony is not one I would choose for someone in the media. To me it sounds somewhat pompous and people never know whether to call you Tony or indeed if both are one and the same person. I owe its use to my first boss Malcolm Messer who, on seeing an article in *The Farmers Weekly* 'by Tony Parkin' exploded, 'I'm not having any office pet names in my paper.'

So Anthony it became and remains, sometimes to my embarrassment, as happened after I had lunched with a well-known farmer and was asked to sign the visitors' book. A heavy leather-bound gilt-edged volume was produced and I found that I was following in the wake of a distinguished collection of professors and agricultural knights. I took the pen and began to sign with my usual flourish but having got halfway through I thought, 'That looks a bit stuffy—after all you've known these people for years. "Tony" would have been more appropriate.' Then to my horror I looked down and found I had written 'Anthony Tony'. The farmer and his wife were standing a discreet distance away in the hall making polite though incoherent noises. What on earth was I to do? I decided to re-work the 'Tony' bit and managed to turn the 'T' into a passable 'P' and the 'o' into an 'a'. Making the 'n' into an 'r' presented greater but not insuperable difficulties but when I got around to converting the 'y' into a 'k' I was in real trouble. All the while my hosts were rocking to and fro from the heels to the balls of their feet no doubt wondering what on earth was going on. Surely the chap could sign his own name, or was he insinuating one of those fulsome pieces about the excellence of the lunch? To make matters worse I was going through one of my phases for using a real fountain pen which was in turn going through one of *its* phases for jetting blobs of ink if one so much as hesitated for a split-second when writing. The result was a right old mess and I am sure my hosts had good reason for wondering whether they had not seriously misjudged me when they rushed back, as I am sure they did, having waved me off, to see what I had done to their book.

I seem to be dogged by Lucky Jim situations ever since the conductress on a crowded Maidstone and District bus managed to get the trigger of her ticket puncher hooked through one of my fly button holes. There was the time when one of my former secretaries and I, on the way back from an OB, stopped for tea. There had been no time for lunch and we were both rather peckish. The place was full and we had to share a table with another girl. The portions were not ample and when the girl got up and went, leaving several sandwiches and scones, we lost no time in finishing them off. Then she returned, presumably from powdering her nose. Fortunately she had a sense of humour. We all burst out laughing and I re-ordered.

But there are some situations when there is nothing, absolutely nothing, you can say which can repair the damage. Such as the occasion on which I hurried out of the old Broadcasting House in Birmingham, having ordered a cab to the station, to find a chap informally clad in a cardigan standing waiting in the yard.

'Are you taking me to the station?' I asked.

He looked astounded. 'What?' he enquired.

'You're not the taxi driver?' I was right. He was not. He was one of our leading television producers paying a state visit from London.

THIRTEEN

Some Of My Best Friends Are Farmers

Why I have left until the last chapter the opportunity to talk about the people with whom I have rubbed shoulders the last thirty-odd years, the farmers themselves, probably speaks for itself. It is not an easy subject on which to generalise which is no doubt why I have found my job over the years so fascinating and at the same time so perplexing. To have made absorbing half-hour programmes with both a man who had brought up seven children on twenty acres in Cornwall and another who was bringing up one son on twenty *thousand* acres in Lincolnshire, both happy and fulfilled in their separate ways, shows how dangerous it is to draw too many conclusions about the genus. Because they were both genuine farmers.

At least once a week I will get into the lift at Pebble Mill to be met with a jocular 'How are the farmers doing these days?' from one of my colleagues. As it takes only twenty seconds or so to reach the fourth floor where I get out I never have time to give an adequate answer, if indeed there is one. One of these days the lift will stick between floors and then I shall be able to say 'Do you mean arable farmers or livestock farmers, and if the latter are you referring to milk producers or pig producers or poultrymen? Are you talking about those in the hills of Merioneth or those on grade one land in Norfolk? The man who bought his land at £2,000 an acre in the late seventies or the chap who inherited it from daddy? Or perhaps you mean a tenant but if so is it the man on an old-fashioned estate paying £25 an acre rent or the one who had to tender £75 to get the tenancy? And are we talking about the fifty-acre farmer or the bloke on five hundred or five thousand acres?'

By this time, with any luck, they will have got the lift going again and my friend will be able to escape at the next floor, regretting that he had ever opened his mouth. But they are fair questions and only the beginning of a series which would need to be answered before a reply could be given to the original bland enquiry. The Ministry of Agriculture may fairly announce that farm incomes went up by forty-five per cent over a twelve-month period but that will not have prevented several farmers going phut during the year, men who have over-extended themselves or simply had a run of bad luck. Many of those with whom I have done programmes are millionaires—you only have to own four or five hundred acres these days to be a millionaire on paper—but others are drawing Family Income Supplement. Again, they are all farmers.

In my job you meet the whole range and experience some unimaginable extremes. One day, for instance, I was given a cup of tea in a Devon farmhouse and asked if I took milk. When I said yes my host fetched a bucket from the other side of the kitchen and gently poured some into my cup. A couple of days later I was drinking twelve-year-old malt whisky out of Waterford glass on a farm in Cheshire. Recently, I was shown to the loo on a holding in West Wales and found myself confronted with the chemical closet familiar from pre-war days while on a farm in East Anglia I was grilled a 16 oz. steak beside a swimming pool in a set-up which would not have been out of place in Beverley Hills. All farmers. There are times when I have felt positively humbled as I have got out of the car in a strange yard carrying my tape recorder and been confronted by the farmer, a bale of hay on his back, his face purple with cold and yet cheerful and welcoming. After recording the interview in the shelter of a building I get back into my warm car—and he shoulders the bale again and sets off across the muddy yard; I talk about it but he actually does it. Equally there have been times when I have felt almost repelled by the luxury and ostentation at the other end of the scale—the half-acre of raked gravel, the display of cars, the heated pool, the hard tennis court and the Jermyn Street shirt. Yet it is quite unwarrantable to make the comparison – it is like comparing the lifestyle of the owner of the village shop with that of the chairman of Tesco – except that, again, these are both farmers, both getting the same price for their milk and both, in all likelihood, members of the same Union.

Like most folk who spend their lives dealing with farmers I suppose I have developed a love–hate relationship with them. You have to admire them for their independence, sturdiness, inventiveness and capacity for hard work, one of the last bastions of free enterprise. But at the same time you realise that they number among their ranks some pretty self-centred, avaricious, unprincipled characters, largely lacking in social conscience.

The trouble is partly historical. Before the last war, during the depression, they were pitied, having had the plug pulled on them in 1921 with the Corn Production (Repeal) Act, and they were subsequently relieved of rates except for a reduced amount on the farmhouse. During the war they were deified for their role in saving us from starvation, although many of them did very well out of it in the process. Since the war they have continued to expect to be treated as a special case in all sorts of ways, ranging from being free to tow trailers without lights to growing as much corn as they like knowing that there is always room for it in the intervention store. I remember going to interview a leading farmer during a very bad drought—so bad that all inessential usage of water had been banned and people had even disconnected their waste pipes to catch the washing-up water to keep their runner beans alive. The man I was visiting was a magistrate who read the lesson in church every Sunday and when he shut his eyes it was night in local agricultural circles. After our chat he showed me round his garden including the shrubbery where three sprinklers were going full blast, off the main. The rules were for other people; he was a farmer. I have no doubt that other people elsewhere were also breaking the rules at that time but a farmer is aided and abetted by the fact that he is usually surrounded by his own land. This enabled a group of farmers whose area was considered for designation as a Site of Special Scientific Interest because it was the breeding habitat of some rare birds to threaten, unofficially, to shoot the lot if the plans went ahead without consultation. There is no certainty that they would have carried out their threat but their special situation meant that they *could* without fear of detection.

This feeling of being in a special category shows up at times in farmers' attitudes towards the *On Your Farm* programme which some of them feel somehow 'belongs' to them. Again, this is a hangover from the wartime and post-war days when BBC programmes were used deliberately to help farmers to produce more food. Since then, however, as I was explaining in Chapter One, pressure groups of all kinds have sprung up and my job nowadays is very much one of holding the ring. A few years ago when some dairy farmers were having a sticky time I mentioned in the programme at the end of a succession of moans that I had telephoned a milk producer in the West Country only to find that he was just off with his family on a Mediterranean cruise. I was threatened with all kinds of fates by farmer listeners including that of being reported to the NFU. One remarked that 'that sort of comment is not worthy of your programme', while another complained 'even if you knew it you need not have broadcast it' and demanded to have more details of the dairy farmer in question whom he assumed wrongly to have several other enterprises. I was able to assure him that the farmer not only earned the whole of his livelihood from milk but that he had started farming on a rented holding only thirteen years earlier with very limited capital. I did not feel it necessary to point out the moral of the story which was that instead of climbing on the expansion bandwagon and borrowing large sums from the bank to do so this man had been content to finance a more gradual increase in cow numbers and facilities out of profits. Which explained why, when others were having difficulty in servicing their overdrafts and paying their feed bills, he was able to have three weeks in the sun. But I did tell the farmer who had complained that I felt it just as relevant to report this story in *On Your Farm* as the tales of woe from other dairy farmers.

Hard as he tries to maintain a fair balance, a radio producer dealing in as sensitive an area as agriculture has now become is bound to upset his listeners from time to time, but I think that if the farmers who feel themselves unfairly treated were to be on the receiving end of some of the letters which land on my desk it would be a revelation to them. A pensioner from Bath, for example, wrote a year or two back:

> I have long considered your programme to be completely biased in favour of the farmers and their inherent conservatism—in fact more often than not it is merely a party political broadcast on behalf of the Tories and the producers ought to be prosecuted under the Trades Description Act. The impression gained over many years of listening to these broadcasts is that farmers are a greedy, unpatriotic, self-interested bunch concerned merely for their own profits and not the least bit interested in food production as such.

And I thought we were striking a balance. Another letter, from Warwickshire, expressed similar sentiments:

> All the farming programmes are clearly sponsored by the farmers, for the farmers and against the interest of the farm workers and consumers.

It would be easy though tedious to dwell on this theme. But equally, I as a producer would be extremely foolish and irresponsible not to take these letters seriously and react to them positively.

I place these comments, which concern the balance and content of our programmes, in a different category from those which reflect attitudes towards farmers themselves based on what listeners have heard in *On Your Farm*. It seems pretty clear from correspondence received over many years that the one thing which the general public finds it difficult to stomach is farmers moaning. This comes over time and time again in letters from all sorts of people from every part of the country. From Northumberland we received the following typical observation:

> Having been involved in and interested in agriculture for about sixty years I listen avidly to your programmes. There is one matter to which I would like to direct your attention because I feel that it does farming no credit. The matter to which I refer occurs too often in the *On Your Farm* programmes. It is the fact that all too often the farmers end up by shaking their begging bowls before the public and telling us how hard is the lot of the farming community from an economic point of view.

A listener from Glasgow, fed up with 'so much grousing and complaining from the "poor" farmers who wanted us all to believe they were living on the breadline' sent us a newspaper cutting showing the large sum left by a local farmer. Meanwhile from Wiltshire:

> Some of us are getting tired of the constant reiteration of the hard-done-by farmers. Last year for weeks we heard how rust was going to reduce seriously the cereal crop. In the end yields were well up to average. This year bad weather was going to affect the crop seriously. In the end yields were almost a record in most areas. It is high time your correspondents should realise that not all your non-farming listeners are foolish enough to believe the 'hard luck' stories of the farming industry.

A letter from Northamptonshire critical of farmers 'whining, moaning and complaining about their imagined hardships' arrived in an envelope addressed to 'On Your Over-prosperous, Fiddling, Tax-evading Farm' while another, from Humberside, included this broadside:

> What a change it would be if some Saturday morning we could hear on the farming programme a farmer telling the truth for once. They have been moaning all their lives, living on their losses. If you want to see the poor farmers you should be in Beverley market on a Wednesday; they roll up in their large cars, no Minis for them, they do their bit of business and then into the pub for the rest of the day. The pubs are open all market day and some of them are so drunk they have to ring up for someone to drive them home.

These, I should emphasise, are not isolated reactions but examples of letters received over a long period from a wide section of the community. A listener from Birmingham pitched in with his contribution in the following terms:

> Never in all the years *On Your Farm* has been broadcast have I heard so much moaning. I always thought that farming was a way of life with its own compensations such as fresh air and freedom and top-quality food which is now a luxury to townfolk even if it were available.

> When a trade union leader speaks out he is called a militant but in my estimation some farmers are worse militants and are destroying the morale of *good* farmers and the goodwill of the rest of the community. One would think, listening to the farmers on your programme, that they are the only section of the community who have to rise early, but there are the postmen, milkmen, newsagents and the old lady pensioners who do office cleaning to mention a few more.

That last point was echoed by a retired farmer, living with his daughter in Crewe, who wrote to say that until he gave up farming he had no idea that other people worked as hard as farmers, many of them getting up at least as early to start their jobs and some doing part-time work in the evenings to make ends meet. Indeed even farmers themselves have been embarrassed sometimes by what they have heard in our programmes. A farm manager from Leicestershire wrote at the height of the 1974 'depression':

> I've been associated with farming since 1949 and I get very tired hearing farmers continually bemoaning the state of agriculture. Ever since I have known it, it has been a profitable business. Today, I venture to suggest that vast profits are being made out of it. Farming should be profitable because it is hard work and there is a lot of capital involved, but why must farmers pretend that it is not so? If things are as bad as they are painted, why is there always such a scramble for land when it is for sale or to let. I know it is a tradition that farmers grumble, but why can't they confine their grumbles to the weather and not let the industry down in full view of the public, grumbling about their imagined losses. If the general public only knew of the profits being made out of agriculture there would be a public outcry. If the farmers on your programme and others cannot stand the heat, they can always get out of the kitchen. As far as I know there is no compulsion to farm.

Again it would be easy to continue this theme but I think that the point has been made. I have been careful to distinguish between the letters reacting to farmers' grumbles over the air and those born out of a more deep-seated jealousy, malice or envy of which we receive quite a number. I feel no useful purpose would be served in publicising them here although they must have had their roots in what has been said in *On Your Farm* over the years.

But generally, there seems to be an enormous reservoir of goodwill towards farmers. By and large the public wants to like them; it does not object to their prospering but what it will not forgive them is whingeing about their lot. Meanwhile a 'dyed in the wool Brummie' who claims not to know a farmer or a farm worker but who does listen to *On Your Farm* leaps to their defence:

> What always amazes me is the number of 'do-gooders' and the amount of 'do-gooding' they intend to do. With what? I can only wonder how anyone who cannot produce his own and his family's food can have the cheek to pass an opinion. I believe that the only people who should talk are the ones who produce (not process) food. How many women or men ever think to say a quiet thank you to a farmer as they pile the food into the supermarket trolley? I never quarrel with the price of food; if you, dear housewife, are not satisfied—try keeping a cow in your back garden. The highest paid workers in the world should be those who produce our food.

The irony is that the actual workers, as opposed to the farmers, are among the lowest paid, as we are not infrequently reminded by our listeners. And yet, what other industry can claim better labour relations than agriculture? Tremendous loyalty, absence of strikes and a productivity record second to none. In what other industry do the employees spend the evening talking about their jobs, boasting about how many acres they have drilled or what lambing percentage they have achieved? I remember taking my tape recorder one night to a herdsmen's discussion group, set up for herdsmen by herdsmen as a forum for exchanging ideas which would enable them to do their jobs better. The farm workers' union – now a trade group of the Transport and General Workers Union – may say what it likes, but that sort of thing is not the product of a dissatisfied workforce.

There is only one fly in the ointment – something which

crops up in conversation every time *On Your Farm* is invited to breakfast by a farm worker's family – and that is the house. The older the worker the larger it looms. This was most noticeable in three recent programmes with farm workers of varying ages. They all referred to the housing factor but the one still in his thirties did not dwell on it; after all he had nearly thirty years ahead of him before he might have to move out of his comfortable 'tied cottage'. The man of forty-eight was beginning to worry while to the third worker the impending prospect of 'going on the Council', as his wife put it, when he retired was a recurrent theme of the conversation across the breakfast table. It is true that following the tied cottage legislation of the seventies the Councils have a responsibility to re-house any farm worker whose house is required for another employee but that does little to reassure the average cowman or tractor driver.

Don Taylor, from Kent, whom we visited for breakfast put it eloquently when speaking of a tribunal he had been sitting on to decide the fate of a fellow farm worker:

> The chap had worked on the farm for forty years and his new boss came before the tribunal and asked for possession of the house and he was like the cat who'd got the cream because he said to us 'I've managed to find alternative accommodation.' When we started questioning as to where this alternative accommodation was, it was ten miles away in the local town and two floors up in a flat. Now, we might just as well have put a black cap on and pronounced death to this chap who'd lived in the village for the whole of his life with all his relations in that village and to do a thing like that to him.

My belief is that if only some way could be found of removing this fear, job satisfaction would make up much of the gap between farm workers' pay and that of industrial workers. As long as they can see folk in other jobs working less hard and less skilfully but nevertheless earning enough to buy their own houses, and so keep pace with inflation, the situation will continue to rankle.

But to return to the subject of farming's image, the National Farmers' Union of England and Wales, which claims to represent more than 80 per cent of the farming population, appears to feel that it needs improving and recently passed unanimously a resolution stating that 'This Annual General Meeting is disturbed by the adverse publicity farmers are receiving in the press and on the media and calls upon Headquarters and the Office Holders of the Union to respond very actively to advise the general public of the true facts.' It is difficult to understand how a Union claimed by its President at the same meeting to be the most effective lobby in the UK, in an industry better served by press, radio and television than any other, can seem to be so misunderstood and misrepresented. Or can it be that it is over-exposed to public gaze; or is it that the public refuses to believe what it is told; or is the NFU simply suffering from paranoia?

It is certainly true that Sir Henry Plumb had a rude shock when he resigned the Presidency of the NFU after nine years and became a Member of the European Parliament. His constituency, the Cotswolds, may sound a nice rural one but it embraces several industrial areas including Cowley and he found somewhat to his surprise that the audiences there were not always as au fait or in sympathy with the pronouncements from Agriculture House, Knightsbridge, as had been the gatherings of farmers which he had been used to addressing.

It is obvious from Sir Henry's experience and from the NFU's concern, not to mention the letters we receive in the *On Your Farm* office, that some people take a delight in farmer-bashing. The curious thing though is that whenever we have tried to gauge the anti-farmer feeling, by sending someone out with a microphone, it seems to evaporate. When the NFU as a result of one of its periodic contemplations of its navel launched the Backbone of Britain Campaign I decided to do some 'vox pop', in other words interview people at random about their attitudes to farmers and farming. The campaign was based on the belief that farmers make an important contribution to the cultural, social and economic life of the country and are the major influence in shaping the rural environment, and it set out to appeal to the general public direct, over the heads of politicians, the media and other agencies. The man in the street was to be invited to meet the farmer on his own patch, face to face.

I sent an interviewer out into the middle of Birmingham to find out the public's reaction and she found herself confronted by a wall of apathy. About eighty per cent of the people she approached had never met a farmer, were not excited by the prospect and really had very little interest in where their food came from or how it was produced. Of the people who did have a view about nine out of ten were wholly sympathetic towards farmers. None of them was destructively critical. I think that the critics are probably few in number but well informed and articulate—and organisations like the NFU and programmes like *On Your Farm* attract them like moths to a candle.

There seem to be three main areas of contention, two of them involving the public at large and one which, although it affects everyone, has arisen as a result of heart-searching among farmers themselves.

The first is intensive livestock keeping sometimes not unfairly called factory farming. The animal welfare lobby is well organised and on the march. From the resolutions put forward for its 1983 AGM it is obvious that the NFU knows that it will not go away and must be confronted. Leaving aside the most extreme cases which would be very difficult for anyone to defend, farmers find themselves in a tricky situation not of their own making. What is happening is that in their attempts to remain competitive they are getting involved in unattractive systems of livestock keeping to provide food for the majority of the consumers who frankly do not really care where it comes from or how it is produced as long as it is cheap. They are being attacked for doing so by a minority who care very deeply and are heavily into anthropomorphism. Many farmers would gladly draw back from ultra-intensive methods if they were able to do so without immediately losing their markets to someone across the Channel, behind the Iron Curtain or further afield. Meanwhile, with rising feeding costs, they are tempted to cram one more bird into each cage and just hope that the inspector does not pay a visit. With certain exceptions, where greed has intervened, they are simply acting as the agents of the great consuming public. But how the impasse created can be resolved, I do not know. Meanwhile the letters, many of them showing signs of careful orchestration, flood into the *On Your Farm* office every time intensive production is mentioned—and frequently when it is not.

I sometimes think that more could be made by farmers of the beneficial side of man's contact with animals in order to counteract the wilder claims of the welfare lobby. Even in the most extensive systems terrible things happen to livestock—wombs are put out, legs are fractured, deformed calves are born, sows lay on their young, situations where the farmer is usually able to bring relief in some form. I remember being told of a scene at my youngest daughter's school.

It was spring and the teacher was telling the class that the lovely woolly lambs would soon be gambolling in the field when Sue put up her hand.

'Please miss, we've had one lamb already.'

The teacher found it hard to contain her excitement. 'Oh, Susan,' she exclaimed, 'you must be thrilled. Come out here and tell the class all about it.'

'It was dead,' she informed her young classmates in a matter-of-fact sort of way, 'and all slimy.'

Complete collapse of teacher whose conception of lambs did not extend beyond the cuddly, skipping stereotype and who had never seen one crawling with maggots or half-eaten by a fox or with its eyes picked out by a crow while it was still alive.

The farmer's intervention has saved untold suffering to livestock from the ravages of disease, accident or the seasons. The big question is how far should the exploitation of the animal for man's benefit be allowed to go. Dehorning of cattle and the breeding of polled strains has prevented a great deal of distress, even in extensive systems of farming, as anyone who has seen a calf which tried to suckle the wrong cow and had its flank ripped open for its pains will appreciate. But can the same argument be used to justify the amputation of pigs' tails?

A poultry farmer outlined his predicament during a debate on the subject at a recent NFU annual meeting. If he kept birds outdoors on free range the foxes took them. After he put them in arks on grass the badgers got underneath the arks and chewed the hens' legs off as they stuck through the wire netting. When he moved them on to deep litter the rats moved in. So he had ended up with them in cages, safe from everything but the welfarists. 'Perhaps,' he added, 'it might help if we took one bird *out* of each cage.' The trouble is, though, that unless every egg producer in the western hemisphere does the same he will be at a disadvantage and find himself undercut in the supermarkets and out of business.

The cruel face of Nature is something of which the extreme welfare lobby is either totally ignorant or finds it convenient to ignore. My wife was delighted when one of her hens brought off thirteen chicks all of which survived. They were left free to wander round the yard, a sight to warm the cockles of any welfarist's heart as the old hen discovered a titbit and called her offspring to her to share it. Then one fine June morning a magpie came and slaughtered nine of them and must have caused the mother a good deal more distress than is suffered by a battery hen in the course of its whole life.

Yet, in the course of my travels with a tape recorder I have been shown things I would rather not have seen. I recall visiting with Michael Clark an establishment where veal calves were kept in narrow stalls under controlled environment in which their bodily functions such as sweating could be manipulated at the flick of a switch. Mike, as humane a farmer as you could find, said: 'I don't know whether you were going to invite me to come and do a programme here but I wouldn't do it even if you asked me.'

The responsible welfare lobby is right to be concerned at what is going on but must temper its concern with understanding as to why it is going on. Farmers must be patient with them, maintain the dialogue and make sure that they do not step beyond the bounds of good livestock husbandry. But as to any long-term solution I despair so long as most folk do not really give a damn where their food comes from and would soon switch to eggs imported from a country with lower welfare standards than ours if they were 2p a dozen cheaper. If there were to be international standards who would monitor them when we cannot even monitor our own?

The second area of controversy comes under the over-used

but convenient heading of conservation. Do not be alarmed, I have no intention of going over again the ground which has been well worked since the publication of Marion Shoard's hard-hitting *Theft of the Countryside* in 1980. Her conclusion was that farmers could not be trusted to look after their land in the interests of the community as a whole and she argued that just as a householder needed planning permission before he could build a porch so the farmer should have to seek approval before he removed a hedge.

It was an overstatement of the case but a very timely one and, in spite of the fury it unleashed in farming circles, will come to be seen as a turning point. Again, farmers have found themselves virtually the victims of circumstance. For twenty years an unholy alliance of the Ministry of Agriculture, the banks, the big firms, economists, consultants and latterly the EEC, was encouraging them to get bigger and produce more. Their natural entrepreneurial instincts rose to the challenge – surely the experts could not all be wrong – and in the process many over-stretched themselves financially. They were forced to do what, in some cases, they knew to be wrong in order to meet their commitments. Meanwhile people were beginning to notice the disappearance of landscape features at the same time as they saw the food mountains beginning to grow and found it difficult to understand why public money was being invested in the removal of their heritage to provide yet more unsaleable food. The trouble was that this sort of movement was difficult to halt in midstream just because the mood of the country appeared to be changing. The bank manager did not stop wanting his money just because Miss Shoard had written a book.

We all have our favourite stories illustrating the developments which have taken place. Mine concerns a young man who bought a big block of moorland cheaply and spent ten years turning it into an oasis. The bank thrust money at him, the Government showered him with grants, the chemical firms stood by with lorry loads of fertiliser, the buildings firms moved in and the young man worked eighteen hours a day. When his son joined him in the business, although by this time with heavy inputs of nitrogen the farm was outyielding many a lowland one, the output was insufficient for two of them so they decided to switch to milk. Another injection of public money helped in the setting up of a dairy and now the milk tanker makes a detour each day to pick up a vast quantity of milk which is made into butter, put into intervention store and then flogged off to the Russians at half price. Meanwhile, the conservationists are objecting to what has happened to their ancient moorland which is now, in their eyes, sullied by a huge bright green blotch. The farmer cannot understand what all the fuss is about. To him it is a major success story; it almost killed him in hard work and nearly bankrupted him at one time but he has made the desert bloom and now has a place worth perhaps twenty times what it was when he took it over.

Farmers are now demanding compensation for not developing their land in ways which would offend the general public. This would seem not unreasonable if they were in some way to be made responsible for the marketing of the extra produce which would be turned off the land were it to be 'improved'. But it seems as irrational to claim compensation as it would be to expect a grant if the extra produce is to add to the mountains and make still further demands on the taxpayer.

The conservation issue will prove just as difficult to resolve as the welfare one and mutual trust and understanding must be the aim of everyone involved rather than the polarisation of views which has been allowed to develop at times. Meantime, the Farming and Wildlife Advisory Groups are extending their influence at the grass roots and having a noticeable effect.

The third subject of concern is one which has worried some people for a great many years but has only recently surfaced within the National Farmers' Union and that is the increase in farm size accompanied by the inevitable decrease in the number of farmers. The disquiet at what has been happening since the war was given voice at the Union's 1982 AGM in a resolution from Somerset and South Avon which deplored the continuing decline in the farming population and considered that the drift towards ever fewer and larger holdings had gone far enough. The resolution was passed unanimously and a working party set up to enquire into what could be done. The situation is that over the last thirty years the average size of farm has more than doubled and the number of farmers has more than halved. Farmers view the trend with concern for two reasons: one is that they are discovering, rather late in the day, the effect that it is having on the social fabric of rural areas in which they live and the other is that the fewer farmers are in actual numbers the weaker their political muscle. What they, collectively, can agree to do about it is another matter since within most – though certainly not all – small farmers is a larger farmer trying to get out. In other words, when the farm next door comes up for sale the chances are that he is in there with a bid, if only to secure extra acres for his son. I suspect that a significant element of the banks' much publicised increased lending to farmers is to enable them to buy land. Indeed, to any farmer paying tax the incentive to buy more land is very powerful since much of the cost is tax-deductible which means that he acquires an appreciating asset largely at the expense of the taxpayer. So it is difficult to see what an organisation governed in the main by larger farmers can recommend to its members.

Travelling between locations in Northern Ireland once on one of our marathon recording trips, David Richardson and I started arguing a hypothetical question posed by the situation we had just left (we both enjoy a good argument). We had visited a thrusting young farmer in his mid-thirties with 200 cows on 200 acres who had admitted during the interview we had just recorded that he would like to expand: the question we were debating was—should he? David's answer was an unequivocal 'yes, of course he should.' My point was that he was already earning plenty of money and that if he bought another hundred acres he would put a farming family off the land for ever. That he would then expensively equip the farm with large grants and finding that the return from the milk failed to repay the bank loans go and lobby his Union into getting the milk price put up. The situation then would be one more family in the dole queue and the consumer paying another penny a pint for his milk. A bit of an exaggeration, perhaps, but it was a good argument although neither of us managed to convince the other.

In case it may be thought that I am a late convert to the

idea of supporting the smaller farmer let me say that my conscience on this is clear. As far back as 1948, with all the brashness of a twenty-two-year-old, I drew up a seven-point plan for farming and the countryside one of the main planks of which was 'guaranteeing a sound future for the small farmer'. (The other six points stand up pretty well, too, after thirty-five years.)

I am not condemning large farms—or at least not those of the kind run by the Parkers in Hampshire or the Whartons in Norfolk and dozens of others. These are farms which generate wealth and jobs for a whole community as opposed to those which simply make money for the farmer and his family, often at the expense of the community. I often think of the wonderful breakfast we had with Jeff Waterfall and his brother, Gerry, on their fen farm near Methwold—another two of the right sort. 'Look,' I said at one stage, 'there are people on this fenland earning a living off three acres and you've got seven hundred and thirty.' To which Jeff replied: 'Ah, but there's a hundred and forty people earning a living off those.' Which was true and what is more the two brothers derived obvious pleasure in farming their land so as to create the maximum amount of employment and prosperity. Compare that with the 1,000-acre wheat field I stood in not long ago. A thousand acres of one variety of wheat, without a hedge, owned by a pension fund and farmed (very well) by an itinerant company. Quite a sight but one which did not contribute a great deal to rural society. It made me think of the man of fifty acres down the valley from me who would not have a bigger farm if you gave it to him. There he has lived a satisfying life, brought up two lovely daughters, and provided a full-time job for one paid man with his dairy cows, pigs and poultry. You could fit twenty farms of his size into that 1,000-acre field.

Although farmers must share the blame for yielding to temptation one cannot help feeling that the Ministry of Agriculture could have done much more to check the large-scale amalgamations which have taken place over the last twenty years instead of encouraging them with its own system of grants and subsidies. Few people would favour any kind of limit on farm size but much could be done through fiscal and pricing mechanisms to achieve the same end, as the Small-farmers' Association has pointed out. The economies of scale begin to peter out after a few hundred acres; beyond that it just becomes more profitable because there are more acres. We are now witnessing the supreme irony, having for years been boasting of our infinitely superior farm structure, of having parties of experts journeying across the Channel to France and Germany to discover the secrets of the small farm.

What a topsy-turvy, engrossing, nettlesome, delectable thing is farming – our biggest and oldest industry – and how privileged I have been to spend thirty years observing and reporting on its fortunes. Thirty years which have seen more change in agriculture and rural life than any similar period since the dawn of time. And what a fascinating, likeable, diverse, infuriating company are farmers and how lucky am I to count so many of them among my friends, along with their workers, landlords, merchants, scientists, vets, advisers and all the others who make up the agricultural scene. Sometimes, at the end of a long, draining day with another to follow I have been known to remark that there must be easier ways of making a living. At other times I pinch myself to make sure it is all true and wonder whether I, perhaps, should be paying the BBC for allowing me to do it rather than the other way round.

In his address to The Farmers' Club following a Nuffield Scholarship spent in studying agricultural broadcasting in various parts of the world Richard Knight, who farms on the Cotswolds, suggested that farming programmes should undergo a 'subtle change of emphasis' to enable them to play more part in removing the misunderstanding which exists between those who grow the food and those who eat it, those who live in the countryside and those who visit it. He may be right in some areas but my impression is that *On Your Farm*, which has run for nearly twenty out of the thirty years I have spent in the agricultural media, has probably moved far enough in this direction and that, as I said earlier, the intelligent layman can learn far more about farmers' fortunes and feelings by 'over-hearing' what they have to say in the programme as it is conceived at present rather than by having it aimed more specifically in their direction. Meanwhile an influential farmer complained to me recently that farming was being over-exposed on radio and television and that what was once a benefit – the relatively large number of farming broadcasts – was in danger of becoming an embarrassment. My answer was that no industry which made such heavy demands on the public purse could object to having its affairs open to public scrutiny, assuming that they were presented fairly and honestly. I could have added, as an additional justification, the attractiveness of the product to the public, for no other industry can provide so rich a seam of raw material for broadcasting as farming and farmers. Others have told me that teletext will do us all out of a job within a decade but I think that they are deluding themselves. How can you put our popular Worcestershire farmer Bill Sinnett, with his gratuitous but pertinent advice to politicians, over on Prestel?

What, finally, has *On Your Farm* achieved over the years? It must have brought a lot of pleasure and some enlightenment to a great many people; it also provides a weekly forum for discussion of all that middle ground where town and country, producer and consumer, taxpayer and subsidy-receiver meet. And I would like to feel that by continually questioning and challenging trends over the years it has helped to put a brake on some of agriculture's more undesirable developments. My unbounded thanks to the thousands of people who have helped the programme on its way.

Index

INDEX